D1681409

Ann Creber
OILS

Ann Creber
OILS

Charles E. Tuttle Company
Rutland, Vermont • Boston • Tokyo

DEDICATION

For my grandmother, Catherine McLeod Summers, who first made me aware of kitchen magic and the lifetime pleasure it imparts, and for my daughter, Cathie Graham, who now shares in her great-grandmother's legacy.

First published in the United States in 1992 by
Charles E. Tuttle Company, Inc. of Rutland, Vermont & Tokyo, Japan,
with editorial offices at 77 Central Street, Boston, Massachusetts 02109

First published in Australia by Angus & Robertson Publishers in 1990

Copyright © Ann Creber 1990

This book is copyright.
Apart from any fair dealing for the purposes of private study, research, criticism or review, as permitted under the Copyright Act, no part may be reproduced by any process without written permission. Inquiries should be addressed to the publishers.

Library of Congress Catalog Card Number 91-66469

ISBN 0-8048-1786-3
ISBN 0-8048-1789-8 (Oils & Vinegars set)

Typeset in 10pt Baskerville by Post Typesetters, Queensland
Printed in Singapore

Contents

ACKNOWLEDGMENTS · vi ·

INTRODUCTION · 1 ·

OLIVE OIL · 4 ·

NUT OILS · 47 ·
Walnut Oil · 47
Hazelnut Oil · 56
Almond Oil · 61
Pistachio Oil · 61

VEGETABLE OILS · 62 ·
Coconut Oil · 64
Avocado Oil · 64

SESAME OIL · 65 ·

PEANUT OIL · 73 ·

SOY OIL · 81 ·

SAFFLOWER OIL · 83 ·

SUNFLOWER OIL · 92 ·

GRAPESEED OIL · 99 ·

CORN (MAIZE) OIL · 104 ·

HERB OILS · 107 ·

INDEX · 110 ·

ACKNOWLEDGMENTS

I would like to extend thanks to Dr Roberto Bertini of Bertolli Oils of Australia Pty Ltd who supplied helpful information on olive oil and also supplied the olive oils I used in recipe development.

Introduction

We've squeezed a great array of oils from nature down the centuries — the ancient Egyptians extracted oil from radishes, the Hittites from almonds. But many people are unaware of the staggering variety available. All living plants contain some oil, but most of it comes from seeds, beans, nuts and fruit, such as the olive. Olive oil was probably the first oil to be produced commercially — the word oil comes from olive. But olive oil totals only five percent of vegetable oil produced throughout the world. You can add a vast selection of other oils to your shelves — or you can pick out those that suit your needs. This book will help you decide.

Oils are divided into three categories according to the type of fatty acids they contain: saturated, monounsaturated and polyunsaturated. Oils that contain significant percentages of both polyunsaturated and mono-unsaturated fatty acids are usually labelled simply "unsaturated". Saturated oils are solid at room temperature, while most unsaturated oils remain liquid above 0°C/32°F. Olive oil solidifies at 2°C/36°F. The more unsaturated an oil is, the more prone it is to oxidation, which causes rancidity. Vitamin E, a natural antioxidant present in some oils such as olive, sunflower and safflower, helps prevent oxidation; light and salt accelerate it. To sum up: All oils should be stored in an airtight container (preferably not plastic) in a cool, dark cupboard.

INTRODUCTION

When oils are heated beyond a certain point — the smoking point — they break down. The danger-point is when a blue haze starts to rise from the oil. Most oils, however, are stable at 200°C/392°F, which is above the temperature required for frying most foods. When frying it is important to have the oil at the right temperature: If too low, the food will be soggy; too high, and it will be brown on the outside while the inside remains uncooked. In general, larger pieces of food such as chicken pieces require lower temperatures (170°C/338°F), smaller pieces, such as chips, require higher temperatures (about 190°C/377°F). If you have a large quantity of food to fry, cook it in batches — if you add too much food the oil temperature will drop and the food will not cook properly.

Fats, including oil, are the richest source of energy in our diet. All oils contain the same number of kilojoules (calories): 370 kilojoules (90 calories) per 10 ml (2 teaspoons). Oils labelled "light" contain the same number of kilojoules: Light simply refers to the flavour.

Polyunsaturated fats have been heavily promoted as a way of reducing cholesterol, but the problem is that they also reduce levels of "good" cholesterol. This "good" cholesterol is high density lipoprotein (HDL), which eliminates "bad" cholesterol (LDL, low density lipoprotein) from the cells and carries it to the liver to be passed out through the bile ducts. Monounsaturated oils are now the most favoured oils because they increase HDL while reducing LDL which clogs the arteries.

VINAIGRETTE

In a classic vinaigrette the usual proportion of oil to vinegar is three parts oil to one vinegar, but in these proportions oil and vinegar soon separate. An emulsion can be formed if two parts oil to one part vinegar are mixed with mustard and crushed plant material (for example, garlic or herbs). The plant cells help separate the oil droplets from each other.

INTRODUCTION

RE-USING OIL

A good-quality oil can be used several times if it has not been overheated, but its smoking point will be lowered with each use. Oil used for cooking fish should be kept separate and re-used only once. To prevent deterioration: Shake off excess batter or coating, which can break off and burn; do not salt food before frying; drain and dry uncoated food to remove excess moisture before frying; before storing, strain used oil to remove any burnt food particles.

Olive Oil

Any amateur enthusiast who has ever tried to make olive oil will have a deep respect for the product bought over the counter.

One such enthusiast of my acquaintance, who freely admits to being a willing victim of nostalgic food writing, was unable to resist olive trees in fruit in a public park and picked many. Unlike the trees in olive groves, these had not been pruned for easy access, and there was much leaping, clutching and falling down, and much wrestling with branches which were straining to return to their natural positions on high. This scene of lone struggle and loss of dignity seemed to be at odds with the balled singing, story telling, steady seasonal rhythms and rustic companionship of the olive harvest frequently described in recipe books and magazines.

Scant hints on the oil making process from a book on preserving borrowed from a local library advised using a small cider mill, and claimed that better quality oil came from green fruit. Without a cider mill of *any* size, and with a basketful of maroon and black/brown fruit, this prospective oil maker felt the initial burst of enthusiasm drain away.

After washing and drying, the olives resisted being squashed, and touching the broken fruit resulted in an instant case of wrinkly hands. She decided that stoneless fruit would be easier to squash, but after hours of pitting, with hands protected by rubber gloves, only a quarter of the olives were done and this paltry amount was whizzed in a food processor. The result was then emptied into layered teatowels, the corners of which were gathered up with heavy string and the whole oozing mess was suspended over a bowl. The dripping of the liquid into the bowl was painfully slow and there appeared to be no oil in sight, just a thick, dark liquid.

Lacking the will and time to remove the stones from the remaining fruit, the weary oil maker tipped them into a bucket and pummelled them with anything to hand. After trying everything from a milk bottle to a newel post, she reverted to rubber-gloved hands and finally a foot (in a well scrubbed rubber boot). Meanwhile, the kitchen was liberally splattered with olive residue and several towels were brought in to mop up the mess and another to drape over the bucket during the pummelling to prevent more splatters.

Next, the stones and pulp were slopped into several layers of folded netting cut in haste from a perfectly good mosquito net, tied with string and suspended over another bowl. With only gravity to work on the pulp, instead of pressure from a press, the collection of oil bearing liquid took ages. Squeezing the fabric-encased olive "puddings" only helped a little and eventually strained the linen of the teatowels to tearing point.

Two days later, a thin pale film of oil appeared on top of both bowls which, although olivey, tasted rather astringent and harsh. The precious oil and some of the accompanying inky liquid were carefully scooped into a glass jar and left for all to admire on the window ledge above the kitchen sink. In all, the yield was about one and a half tablespoonsful. The cost included several tea towels which were stained beyond redemption, the mosquito net, two towels which were ripped up for household rags, and many hours of frustrating labour.

Next one of the sons of the family — who had been absent during the oil making — entered the kitchen in a rare (but brief) tidying-up mood and before he could be restrained tipped the contents of the jar down the sink, rinsed the jar and placed it in the dishwashing machine. At this stage, the oil maker became a muttering wreck.

The oil collected had an inferior taste — although definitely a "first" and "cold" pressing (or, more precisely, a cold *dripping*) — and would not have been given the "Extra Virgin" status accorded to the best oils by the International Olive Oil Council.

Why was it not better? There are several reasons: the trees were grown in a subtropical region which had experienced a very wet late summer and autumn, and the fruit was picked in late autumn and was probably waterlogged and too ripe. Further, olive oil production is a highly specialised industry in which quality is directly related to experience, tradition, type of olive, climate, the ripeness of the fruit and its condition, and controlled methods of extraction (which these days involve stainless steel drums and centrifuging instead of presses, mats and syphons).

In current commercial production some things have not changed. There is no better way to harvest olives than by hand and, at the time of prime ripeness, many hands are needed. In some areas, goat horns are pushed on the ends of fingers to assist the pickers in removing the fruit: by scrabbling at branches with these "claws" efficiency is considerably increased. Nets spread beneath the trees catch the olives which are then gathered into boxes and baskets and delivered to the mill.

Once extracted the oil is graded according to standards set by the Madrid based IOOC (International Olive Oil Council) and several terms are used to describe quality of the product.

"Virgin" olive oil is obtained from the fruit of the olive tree without using heat during extraction: the olives are not subjected to any treatment other than washing, filtering, decanting or centrifuging.

"Cold pressed" olive oil describes the old method of collection, although in modern plants the slow pressing stage has been replaced by a continuous action process with olives going in one end and the oil being spun off at the other. The good news is that quality suffers in no way from the new methods of extraction: in fact, it is enhanced.

"Extra Virgin" olive oil has the highest quality taste and aroma, with a maximum acidity of 1 percent. It is the low acidity which is the key to olive oil quality. For example "Virgin" olive oil has a good flavour but its acidity can be as high as 3 percent.

"Olive Oil" or "100 percent Pure Olive Oil" is a blend of refined virgin olive oil and "Virgin" and/or "Extra Virgin" olive oil. The refined virgin olive oil is made by removing impurities from oils which do not meet the standards of the "Virgin" or "Extra Virgin" class. Refining reduces the acidity and produces a product which is more bland. To restore the distinctive flavour, colour and aroma of the oil, some unrefined virgin oil is blended back into it. "Extra Light" or "Light" olive oils belong to this category and sometimes have a light and "indistinct" taste.

The olive *(Olea europaea)* first appeared in western Asia, but the scrubby, thorny bush which was the wild olive of Syria and Palestine bore little resemblance to today's heroic and stately trees. In ancient times olive oil also lit lamps, ignited waning fires, anointed heads of state, was offered up to gods and was used in cosmetics and unguents.

Inhabitants of the British Isles, and of the more northerly parts of Europe, although not total strangers to olive oil, did not embrace it at table until after the Second World War when mobility and migration gave the western world a richer mix of people, food and culture. A small bottle of olive oil may have been kept in medicine cabinets as a salve for nappy rash and for home-made beauty treatments, but the oil of the noble olive was rarely found in the kitchen.

Olive oil consumption is rising worldwide with the Greeks maintaining a healthy lead over all countries. Production also continues to increase, with the Spaniards making more than any other nation.

Nominating the best olive oil would be difficult, even for an impartial expert, and there is much healthy competition between countries and regions for this particular honour. The choice of "best" olive oil is very much a case of personal preference.

Tastings at gourmet shops and fine food halls have given interested parties opportunities to sample a range drawn from the large commercial producers as well as the smaller concerns.

As well as being a sensuous marvellous food, olive oil has health giving properties.

Back in 1953, medical researchers realised that people in Mediterranean countries had low levels of coronary heart disease. Although they noted that the Mediterranean diet was rich in olive oil, they assumed the major health benefits were due to the low level of saturated fats. For the next 30 years or so, medical research and dietary advice to the public concentrated on reducing saturated fats and replacing them with polyunsaturated fats. However, several long-term studies showed that although more polyunsaturates could reduce incidence of heart disease, the overall death rate was not changing much. People were simply dying of cancer instead of heart disease.

Going back to their original Mediterranean studies, researchers noted that people from these areas had a low incidence of heart disease *and* a low incidence of cancer. Rather than looking at what Mediterranean people did not eat, researchers began to look at what they did eat: lots of vegetables, legumes, grains, fish and olive oil.

Further research has shown that olive oil has some very clear benefits such as reducing total cholesterol without reducing the "good" HDL cholesterol which gives protection against heart disease. This is in contrast to some polyunsaturated oils which reduce both the "good" and "bad" cholesterol.

Also, in order to resist cancer-causing agents, people from Anglo-Saxon and northern European backgrounds need a different balance of fatty acids in cell membranes. More fish plus olive oil seems to be the ideal combination.

Natural antioxidants such as vitamin E are present in olive oil and these prevent the oil becoming rancid and the fats oxidising to form substances which can damage cell membranes.

The method of extracting the oil from the olives also plays its part in health and in environmental conservation. Oil is expressed from the fruit without the use of heat and this prevents any derangement of the fatty acids and preserves the antioxidants present. This heatless method of collecting the oil is environmentally desirable because no chemical solvents are involved.

As far as cooking is concerned, olive oil can be heated to a much higher temperature than other oils without damaging its fatty acids. Olive oil also forms a seal around food so that less fat is absorbed into any food being fried.

Eating is a pleasure and a necessity. Olive oil fulfills the roles of enjoyment and replenishment because it tastes wonderful and it is good for you. Thousands of years of history are proof of the health benefits of olive oil, and Mediterranean cuisine is proof of the pleasure.

Seafood · Patties · with · Tartar · Sauce

Serve these savoury little morsels with pre-dinner drinks. They may also be served as a first course, but of course the quantity could be reduced.

4 slices slightly stale white bread (about 125 g; 4 oz)	250 g (8 oz) crayfish meat, coarsely chopped
1 garlic clove, coarsely chopped	250 g (8 oz) peeled prawns (shrimps), chopped
1 small onion, thickly sliced	¼ cup (4 fl oz) mayonnaise (see Tartar Sauce, below)
1 tablespoon olive oil	1 large egg
1 tablespoon coarsely chopped parsley	1 tablespoon white wine vinegar or lemon juice

OILS

Grind the bread to crumbs in a food processor; set aside about ¼ cup (1 oz) for coating the patties.

Place the garlic and onion in a food processor and finely chop. Heat the oil in a skillet. Add the garlic and onion and sauté until pale gold.

Combine the reserved breadcrumbs, garlic/onion mixture, parsley, crayfish, prawns, mayonnaise, egg and vinegar in the processor. Using the stop/start switch, process only until mixture is well blended but still fairly coarse.

With lightly floured hands, shape the mixture into small patties about 3.75 cm (1½ inches) across. Coat with the crumbs and place on a well buttered baking tray. (If convenient, tray may be covered and chilled at this stage.)

Bake in a preheated 190°C (375°F) oven for 12 to 15 minutes, or until golden brown. Serve with Tartar Sauce.

Tartar Sauce

1 large egg
1 tablespoon mild mustard
3 tablespoons lemon juice
1¼ cups (10 fl oz) extra-light olive oil
Freshly ground pepper
1 tablespoon grated onion
3 small sour dill pickles
1 tablespoon drained capers, rinsed
1 teaspoon prepared horseradish
Few drops of Tabasco sauce

To make the mayonnaise by hand, combine the egg, mustard, 1 tablespoon of the lemon juice, 1 tablespoon of olive oil and the pepper. Blend together until smooth, then very gradually — one drop at a time — add the remaining olive oil, stirring constantly. When the mixture begins to emulsify, the oil may be poured in a thin even stream, stirring or whisking all the time. Stir in the remaining lemon juice. (Reserve ¼ cup (4 fl oz) for the Seafood Patties.) Add the grated onion, very finely chopped gherkin and finely chopped capers. Stir in the horseradish and the Tabasco sauce.

If using a food processor or blender, combine the egg, mustard, 1 tablespoon of the lemon juice, 1 tablespoon of the olive oil and the pepper in the processor bowl. Process until blended. With the motor running, pour the remaining oil through the feeding tube in a thin steady stream; add the lemon juice. (Reserve ¼ cup (4 fl oz) for the Seafood Patties.) Add the onion, pickles, gherkin, capers, horseradish and Tabasco sauce. Process for about 10 seconds, until smooth. Spoon into a container, cover and chill until required.

Makes about 48 patties

Supreme · Open · Sandwich

It is the tapenade which gives this sandwich its zing. Great munching.

2 thick slices cut lengthwise from a French loaf
2 tablespoons Tapenade (see recipe, page 12)
1 large tomato, thinly sliced
4 thin slices prosciutto
Wafer-thin slices of onion (red onion, preferably)

Lightly toast the bread on each side. Spread 1 tablespoon of the tapenade onto each slice. Arrange tomato slices on top; "flop" prosciutto slices on top. Garnish with a couple of onion rings on each. Serve with a knife for easier eating!

Serves 2

OILS

Spiced · Hard-boiled · Eggs

After meeting our guide in the marketplace at Jerusalem before heading off for the Dead Sea, he queried whether we had eaten. It was 6.30 a.m. and we hadn't, so he led us to a small spice-fragrant shop and bought breakfast for us. An improbable breakfast for Western palates but wonderful, it consisted of spicy fried hard-boiled eggs, chewy flat bread and fresh dates.

6 hard-boiled eggs
Olive oil
2 tablespoons crushed cumin seed
1 tablespoon ground cinnamon
1 tablespoon ground turmeric
1 tablespoon sea salt or other coarse salt
Ground white pepper

Peel the eggs as soon as they are cool enough to handle, prick the whites with a needle or fine skewer right through to the yolks. These need to be pricked quite generously to prevent the eggs bursting open.

Pour sufficient olive oil into a small pan to cover the base and heat until quite hot but not smoking. Add the eggs and cook, turning often to prevent burning. Remove when they are golden all over, about 5 minutes.

Mix together the spices, salt and pepper and roll the eggs in the mixture whilst still hot. If preferred, the eggs may be fried as above and the spicy mixture passed separately, but it is traditional to cook them as suggested in the recipe.

Tapenade

Perhaps the most appetising of all spreads, this very savoury version is easily made and will keep well. Serve it as a spread or with vegetable crudités.

6 anchovy fillets, soaked in a little milk
200 g can (6½ oz) tuna in oil, drained
12 black olives, pitted and chopped
½ cup (4 fl oz) extra-virgin olive oil
1 or 2 garlic cloves, crushed
6 capers, rinsed and drained

OLIVE OIL

       2 teaspoons lemon juice   Freshly ground pepper
       1 teaspoon mild mustard   Dash of brandy (optional)

Drain the anchovy fillets; rinse lightly. (This soaking in milk removes excessive saltiness.)

    Roughly chop the anchovies and place into the bowl of a food processor with all of the other ingredients. Blend to the preferred consistency; spoon into a bowl. Serve with breads or vegetable crudités. If tapenade is to be kept for a few days, cover well and chill.

Serves 4 to 6

NOTE: For a more traditional preparation, chop all ingredients finely and mix well with a fork rather than using a food processor.

Hummus

Another popular Israeli dish which uses chick peas (garbanzo beans), it very much depends on the quality of the olive oil used for its flavour and consistency. In Israel it was served in most private homes we visited as well as in restaurants. Eaten as an appetiser, dip or first course, it was always presented spread on a plate, topped with a little additional olive oil and garnished with a sprinkle of paprika and chopped parsley.

      2 cans (each 500g; 1 lb)   6 tablespoons (3 fl oz)
        chick peas (garbanzo   virgin or extra-virgin
        beans), or 750 g (1½ lb)   olive oil
        dried garbanzo beans   Salt (optional)
        soaked overnight and   Freshly ground pepper
        well drained $1/3$ teaspoon paprika
      1 garlic clove, minced   2 tablespoons tahini
      5 to 6 tablespoons fresh   Very finely chopped
        lemon juice   parsley

Drain the canned or cooked beans. Put them through a fine mincer twice or purée in a food processor with the garlic. Mix in the lemon juice and olive oil, one tablespoon at a time, stirring well after each addition. Add the salt, pepper and paprika and mix thoroughly. Finally, stir in the tahini, blending well.

To serve, place a mound of the mixture onto 6 salad or small dinner plates. Press the back of a spoon gently on to the mound, turning the plate to evenly spread out the hummus, forming a slight "wall" around the outer edge. Drizzle a little olive oil into the centre of the hummus, sprinkle on a dash of paprika and a little chopped parsley. Serve with torn or cut pita bread to scoop up the hummus. Delightful!

Serves 6

Garlic · Soup

There are many versions of this recipe; this is a simple prepared one which offers a robust garlic flavour that is not confused with a multitude of other ingredients.

12 garlic cloves	*2 tablespoons extra-virgin*
1 l (32 fl oz) water	*olive oil*
Sprig of thyme	*1 cup (4 oz) grated tasty*
Sprig of sage	*(sharp or Jack) cheese*
Salt (optional)	*12 slices day old French*
Plenty of pepper	*breadstick*

Crush all of the garlic. Combine the garlic, water, thyme, sage, salt and pepper in a pan and bring to a boil. Boil for 20 minutes.

Strain the liquid through a fine strainer into a heated casserole. Stir in the oil. Sprinkle the French bread with the cheese. Place the bread on the soup.

Bake in a moderate oven 185°C (375°F) until the bread has absorbed some of the liquid and the cheese is bubbling hot.

Serves 6 to 8

Cioppino

This beautiful Italian stew (or soup? take your choice!) must not be over-cooked or the fish will become dry and "woolly". Cooked as it should be, it is a quickly prepared meal for a busy day.

¼ cup (2 fl oz) virgin olive oil	4 cups (32 fl oz) water or light fish stock
1 medium onion, chopped	1 cup (8 fl oz) dry white wine
1 garlic clove, finely chopped	500 g (1 lb) fish fillets, cut into large chunks (choose firm-fleshed fish)
500 g (1 lb) canned tomatoes	
Freshly ground pepper	250 g (8 oz) green prawns (shrimps), peeled and deveined
1½ tablespoons shredded basil leaves	

Heat the oil in a large heavy-based saucepan. Sauté the onion and garlic until the onion is translucent. Add the tomatoes and the juices from the can, pepper, basil and water. Reduce the heat, cover the saucepan and simmer gently for about 30 minutes. Stir once in a while.

Add the wine, fish and, if necessary, another ½ to 1 cup (4 to 8 fl oz) water. Return to a boil, reduce the heat and simmer for about 5 minutes, stirring from time to time.

Add the prawns. Cover and cook gently for about 5 minutes or until the prawns turn pink.

Ladle into large bowls (old-fashioned, rimmed soup plates look wonderful) and serve at once. Serve a basket of crusty bread for mopping up.

Serves 4 to 6

Baked · Potato · Skins · with · Aïoli

A friend who knows I'm mad about potatoes brought this recipe from America for me. And it is WONDERFUL!

6 medium potatoes	Coarse salt (I like to use Maldon sea salt)
3 tablespoons melted butter	

Aïoli

Pulp of 2 baked potatoes	⅔ cup (5⅓ fl oz) virgin
6 garlic cloves, crushed or	olive oil
very finely chopped	1 small egg yolk
	1 teaspoon lemon juice

Scrub the potatoes, rinse and pat as dry as possible. Prick the skin in several places with a sharp fork or metal skewer and place potatoes on a baking tray.

Bake in a 180°C (375°F) oven for 50 to 60 minutes, or until tender. Allow to cool a little. Cut in half lengthwise and scoop out pulp, leaving a shell approximately 1 cm (½ inch) thick. Reserve the cooked pulp from 2 potatoes to make the Aïoli.

Cut each shell lengthwise into 3 equal sections. Brush the shells inside and out with the melted butter; sprinkle with a little crushed salt. Bake the shells on an oven tray in a 250°C (450°F) oven for 10 to 12 minutes, or until crisp.

To make the sauce, combine the reserve potato pulp with the garlic and half of the oil in a food processor or blender. Blend until quite smooth. Add the egg yolk, gradually add the remaining oil and lemon juice. If too thick, add a little boiling water and stir well.

Serve with the hot, crisp potato skins for dipping.

Serves 6

Asparagus · Vinaigrette

Along with daffodils, apple blossoms and hyacinths, the first pale asparagus spears herald the return of spring, and their arrival should be celebrated with due ceremony. I love to serve this delicacy at room temperature with a simple sauce of butter, lemon juice and pepper or with this smooth vinaigrette.

1 kg (2 lb) young asparagus spears

Vinaigrette

6 tablespoons (3 fl oz)	wine or red wine vinegar
virgin or light olive oil	1 teaspoon Dijon mustard
1 to 1½ tablespoons white	½ teaspoon sugar

Steam the asparagus spears for 7 to 8 minutes. Drain well. Serve at once with the butter sauce or vinaigrette.

To make vinaigrette: Whisk all ingredients together until well blended.

Serves 6 to 8

NOTE: To ensure tender asparagus, snap off the woody base of the stem where it breaks naturally when bent between both hands.

Shakshouka

I first encountered this tasty dish on a recent visit to Israel and loved it! Great for an easy lunch or even a late weekend breakfast.

⅓ cup (2⅔ fl oz) olive oil	1 cup (8 fl oz) chicken stock
2 medium onions, coarsely chopped	2 tablespoons tomato paste
6 garlic cloves, crushed or finely chopped (less, if you prefer)	3 to 4 drops Tabasco sauce
	⅓ cup (2 oz) pitted and sliced green olives
4 medium tomatoes, peeled and chopped	¾ teaspoon ground cumin
	½ teaspoon freshly ground black pepper
2 small red or green capsicums (bell peppers), seeded and diced	4 to 6 eggs

Heat the olive oil in a skillet. Add the onions and sauté until golden brown. Add the garlic and stir-fry. Stir in the tomatoes and capsicums. Cover and cook for about 10 minutes. Add the chicken stock, tomato paste, Tabasco and olives. Season with cumin and pepper. Cook slowly, stirring occasionally, for 25 to 30 minutes.

Pat down the vegetables into a smooth layer. Break the eggs into the pan, taking care to ensure that each is intact and evenly spread on the vegetable base. Cover the pan and cook gently until eggs are quite firm.

Each serving should include an egg and some sauce. (If using small eggs, serve two for each portion.)

Serves 4 to 6

Marinated · Goat · Cheese with · Roasted · Capsicums (Bell Peppers)

Serve as part of a generous antipasto or as a light luncheon with Italian sausage or prosciutto. Make sure there is plenty of bread for mopping up the luscious oil!

125 to 150 g (4 to 5 oz) fresh goat cheese or 4 individual cheeses
¾ teaspoon lightly crushed black peppercorns
2 or 3 small slivers of garlic
1 generous sprig of thyme
1 bay leaf, torn in several places
2 red capsicums (bell peppers)
2 yellow capsicums (bell peppers)
Olive oil (classic or extra-virgin)

Place the goat cheese in a jar. Add peppercorns, garlic, thyme and bay leaf. Pour on sufficient olive oil to generously cover the cheeses. Allow to marinate for at least 24 hours.

Grill (broil) the capsicums until they are well charred. Place in a plastic bag, seal and set aside for about 15 minutes. After that time, the skin will peel off very easily. Halve and seed and derib the capsicums.

Place the prepared capsicums into a jar; pour on olive oil to cover. Marinate for at least 24 hours. Cut into strips.

Serve the cheeses garnished with strips of pepper, olives and lots of bread. It is wonderful with foccacio.

Serves 4

Herbed · Goat · Cheese · in · Olive · Oil

This is a recipe in which you can choose whichever olive oil you prefer and still enjoy superb flavour. I love to use extra-virgin olive oil, but perhaps you would prefer to use the extra-light variety. Whatever your preference, this is a wonderful food to serve as part of a buffet spread. Begin preparation a couple of days ahead of serving to allow the flavours to blend and mellow. Small individual cheeses may be used or larger ones cut into portions.

250 g (8 oz) goat cheese
2 tablespoons very finely chopped rosemary
2 teaspoons finely grated lemon zest.
1 small garlic clove, finely chopped or slivered
Freshly ground black pepper
½ cup (4 fl oz) olive oil
Witlof (Belgian endive) leaves
Cherry tomatoes
Fresh herb sprigs
Crusty Italian bread

Place the cheese in a dish just large enough to arrange it in a single layer. Sprinkle on the chopped rosemary, lemon zest, garlic and pepper. Drizzle the oil on top, ensuring cheese is evenly covered. Cover the dish and refrigerate, turning cheese occasionally.

To serve, allow the cheese to reach room temperature. Remove the cheese from the oil marinade with a slotted spoon and arrange on a serving platter. Strain the marinade and pour over cheeses.

Garnish with fresh rosemary sprigs; serve with witlof leaves, cherry tomatoes and generous quantities of chunky bread — serve plenty for dipping into the glorious olive oil!

Serves 8 to 10

NOTE: Introduce a change of flavour by substituting thyme, mixed herbs or mint for rosemary.

French · Breadstick · Pizza

This is a glamorous version of grilled cheese and tomato. Serve it with a crisp salad to complete a fast, light and tasty meal.

100 g (3½ oz) peperoni salami, cut into thin strips
125 g (4½ oz) mozzarella cheese, sliced
2 ripe tomatoes, sliced
½ garlic clove, crushed
1 small French loaf, sliced lengthwise
3 tablespoons extra-virgin olive oil
6 black olives, stoned and slivered
2 to 3 anchovy fillets, very finely chopped or slivered

Prepare the salami, cheese and tomatoes and garlic. Generously moisten the cut surface of the top half of the bread with olive oil.

Arrange the salami slices, cheese, tomato, garlic, olives and anchovies on bottom half of the cut loaf.

Cook under a hot grill (broiler) until the cheese melts. Place top back onto the bread and press down. Cut into thick slices to serve.

Serves 2

Suppli · with · Olives · and · Artichokes

I first tasted *suppli* during a "weekend in the country" on the property of a town-based friend. Dr Roberto Bertini, Australia-based Managing Director or Italian Bertolli Oils, cooked his version of this traditional dish for us — and we loved it. Just remember that the oil must be *HOT!*

1 white onion, finely chopped	2 tablespoons finely grated Parmesan cheese
2 tablespoons virgin olive oil	2 eggs, lightly beaten
250 g (9 oz) white rice	3 anchovy fillets, mashed or finely chopped
½ cup (4 fl oz) dry white wine	185 g (6 oz) mozzarella or provolone cheese, cubed
2 cups (16 fl oz) rich chicken stock	185 g (6 oz) dry breadcrumbs
Pinch of saffron	Olive oil, for deep frying
Freshly ground pepper	

To prepare *suppli*, sauté the onion in the heated oil until softened but not browned. Add the rice and cook well. Add the wine, half of the stock, the saffron and pepper. Bring slowly to a boil, stirring constantly. When the liquid has almost evaporated, add the remaining 1 cup (8 fl oz) stock. Reduce the heat and continue cooking, uncovered, until the liquid has all been absorbed and the rice is barely tender. Stir in the grated Parmesan and set aside to cool.

Add beaten eggs and anchovies to the rice mixture and stir in gently. Take a small tablespoon of the rice mixture and work it around each cube of mozzarella until it is enclosed.

Roll the balls in the breadcrumbs. Chill for 1 hour.

Deep-fry the *suppli* in hot oil in small batches until crisp and golden. If preferred, *suppli* may be made in advance and frozen until required. To use, thaw for 30 minutes at room temperature. Deep fry for a further 5 minutes until cooked through. (The best way of testing is to cut one in half.)

To serve, garnish with stuffed olives and marinated artichoke hearts.

Serves 4

Falafel

When I was in the Middle East recently, I discovered that falafel appears to be the favoured fast food of the region. It is claimed that the best of all falafel is served in a kiosk at the Haifa bus station; we tried it and it certainly must rate highly. One edge had been nipped from the saucer-size pita bread, to form a pocket in which a generous scoop of falafel balls had been spooned, and the only limitation as to the quantity of salad was imposed by how much you could tuck into the bread and still manage to get your mouth around! Bowls of very good tahini and hummus were there to be spooned onto the salads, so by the time the final creation was completed it was almost as substantial as a three-course meal.

This is another excellent version of the falafel we ate in Tel Aviv.

500 g (1 lb) dried chick peas (garbanzo beans)	1 teaspoon ground cumin
2 teaspoons baking soda	1 teaspoon ground coriander (cilantro)
2 tablespoons burghul (bulgur; cracked wheat)	½ teaspoon finely ground pepper (less, if preferred)
2 slices white bread	
3 garlic cloves, chopped	1 teaspoon sweet paprika
2 tablespoons chopped parsley	3 tablespoons dried breadcrumbs
1 teaspoon salt (optional)	

Soak the beans overnight in a large quantity of cold water to which the soda has been added. Next day, rinse and drain well. Mince or coarsely purée in a food processor. Transfer to a large mixing bowl.

Place the burghul into a bowl, pour on boiling water and let stand for 20 minutes.

Moisten the bread, then squeeze dry and purée with the garlic and parsley. Add to the chick peas.

Drain the burghul well, squeezing it as dry as possible in a teatowel or muslin cloth. Add the burghul, salt, cumin, coriander, pepper and paprika to the chick peas. Stir in. Add the dried breadcrumbs and mix well. Allow to stand for 20 minutes. With slightly dampened hands, form the mixture into balls about the size of a walnut, flattening each slightly.

Heat about 10 cm (4 inches) of light olive oil in a deep fryer. Fry the balls until golden brown on both sides. Drain well on paper towels. Spoon about 5 balls into prepared pita bread pockets. Serve them with a selection of mixed salad ingredients, olives, dill pickles, tahini, hummus, shredded lettuce, etc.

A very satisfying and substantial snack or an interesting change for weekend lunches.

Makes about 70 balls

Pasta · Salad · with · Pecan · Pesto

On one occasion when I was short of pine nuts but had plenty of pecans, I made a substitute version of pesto; it worked well, and I often use it now instead of the more traditional recipe.

3 cups (5 oz) well-packed fresh basil leaves
Few sprigs of Italian parsley, chopped
2 large garlic cloves
Salt (optional)
½ cup (2 oz) pecans, chopped
¼ cup (1 oz) pine nuts
¾ cup (6 fl oz) virgin olive oil
¾ cup (3 oz) freshly grated Parmesan cheese

Salad

750 g (1½ lb) cooked spiral pasta, well drained
4 small zucchini (courgettes), cut into julienne
1 red onion, thinly sliced
1 cup (16 whole) cherry tomatoes
2 tablespoons chopped parsley
Freshly ground black pepper

OLIVE OIL

To make the pesto, use a food processor with the metal blade; combine basil leaves, parsley, garlic and salt and process until finely chopped. Add the pecans, pine nuts and oil and purée until well blended. Add the cheese and process until mixed in. Spoon into a bowl or jar until required. (If it is not needed for a few days, pour a little olive oil onto the surface; stir this into the pesto before using.)

Place the cooked pasta in a large bowl. Add the zucchini, onion, cherry tomatoes, parsley and pepper to taste. Spoon or pour on the pesto; mix lightly but thoroughly, until pasta is well coated. Serve salad at room temperature.

Serves 10

Spaghetti · with · Tomatoes · and · Basil

This beautiful dish captures the essence of an Italian summer — rich, red tomatoes, fragrant basil and sharp Parmesan mingle with voluptuous extra-virgin olive oil to transform a simple pasta meal into a memorable one.

750 g (1½ lb) firm ripe red tomatoes
½ garlic clove, very finely chopped
6 tablespoons (3 fl oz) extra-virgin olive oil
Juice of ½ lemon
⅓ cup (12 leaves) basil leaves
Salt (optional)
Freshly grated black pepper
500 g (1 lb) spaghetti
Freshly grated Parmesan

Blanch the tomatoes; peel and quarter them and discard the seeds. Cut the flesh into largish pieces.

Place the tomatoes into a bowl with the garlic, olive oil, lemon juice and half the basil leaves, torn into small pieces. (They discolour more easily if cut, rather than torn.) Add a little seasoning to taste. Set aside for at least 30 minutes; do not chill. Cook the spaghetti in lightly salted boiling water until al dente. Drain well.

Pour the tomato/oil mixture over the pasta and toss well. Sprinkle on the grated Parmesan and the remainder of the basil leaves, torn just before serving.

Serves 4 to 6

NOTE: This makes an excellent starter.

Marinated · Garfish · Fillets

One of the sweetest-fleshed of all fish, the garfish is often rejected because of its multitude of fine bones. Ask your fishmonger to fillet them for you and this problem will be solved.

12 garfish (soft, white-fleshed fish) fillets

Marinade

6 tablespoons (3 fl oz) olive oil	2 tablespoons very finely chopped parsley
1 small onion, finely chopped	1 tablespoon finely chopped dill
4 garlic cloves, crushed	Freshly ground pepper

Arrange the fish fillets in a flat dish. Mix together the marinade ingredients and pour over the fillets.

Cover the dish and allow to chill overnight. Serve with fresh dill sprigs, lemon wedges and lightly buttered rye bread.

Serves 6

Lemon-marinated · Prawns (Shrimps)

The refreshing combination of flavours provides an excellent first course for a summer dinner party.

4 lemon slices	2 teaspoons sugar
2 bay leaves	½ teaspoon mustard seeds
Crushed peppercorns	3 drops Tabasco sauce
32 small green prawns (shrimps)	¼ teaspoon coarsely ground pepper or seasoned pepper
2 large ripe tomatoes, peeled, seeded and very finely chopped	Small lettuce leaves or witlof (Belgian endive) leaves
1 garlic clove, finely chopped	1 lemon, thinly sliced
½ cup (4 fl oz) extra-light olive oil	1 red onion, thinly sliced
⅓ cup (2⅔ fl oz) fresh lemon juice	

In a saucepan, combine the lemon slices and bay leaves with ¾ cup (6 fl oz) of lightly salted water; and several coarsely crushed peppercorns. Bring the water to the boil. Add the prawns and cook for only 1 to 2 minutes or until they turn pink and are slightly firm to the touch. Drain in a colander, refresh under running cold water. Remove shells and sand veins.

Combine the tomatoes, garlic, oil, lemon juice, sugar, mustard seeds, Tabasco and pepper in a bowl. Mix well. Toss the prawns into the marinade and chill, well covered, for at least 8 hours.

Arrange the salad greens on plates. Spoon on the prawns and some of the marinade. Garnish plates with lemon and onion slices and serve with wafer-thin slices of buttered wholemeal bread.

Serves 4

Tasmanian · Salmon · Tartare

Our magnificent Atlantic salmon is almost too good to cook! Serve it raw and appreciate its texture and flavour. I feel it is best to cut it by hand rather than to use a food processor, which tends to make it a little pulpy. Use a virgin olive oil rather than the rich and fruitier extra-virgin olive oil — its flavour tends to cloud that of the delicate fish.

1 kg (2 lb) fresh Tasmanian or Atlantic salmon
2 tablespoons very finely chopped Italian parsley
1 tablespoon capers, rinsed and drained (use more if you prefer a sharper flavour)
2 tablespoons fresh chopped chives

½ cup (4 fl oz) virgin olive oil
3 tablespoons lemon juice (more or less, to taste)
2 teaspoons Dijon mustard
2 to 3 drops Tabasco sauce
Freshly ground black pepper
Triangles of black bread, dark rye or pumpernickel

Cut the salmon into pieces. Cut up very finely to the consistency of coarse mincemeat. Place in a bowl; add the parsley, capers and chives and toss lightly.

Mix together the oil, lemon juice, mustard and Tabasco sauce and pour into the salmon mixture. Using two forks, toss together very lightly. Taste, and add pepper; mix lightly again. Serve with breads as suggested.

Makes about 3 cups (24 oz)

Prawns (Shrimps) · Pil · Pil

A dish that is popular in the south of Spain, this transposes well to the Australian lifestyle. Serve it as an interesting appetiser or as part of a casual buffet spread.

500 g (1 lb) lightly cooked prawns (shrimps), shelled but with tails intact
Cayenne pepper
½ cup (4 fl oz) extra-virgin olive oil
Fresh Italian bread
Vinegar (optional)

Place the prepared prawns in a shallow ovenproof dish and sprinkle lightly with the cayenne pepper. Pour on the oil and place under a hot grill (broiler) for 8 to 10 minutes. (There will probably be a bit of spattering.)

Serve at once with lots of bread for mopping up the superb juices. Pass vinegar separately for those who like a dash of it to add zest to this dish.

Serves 4

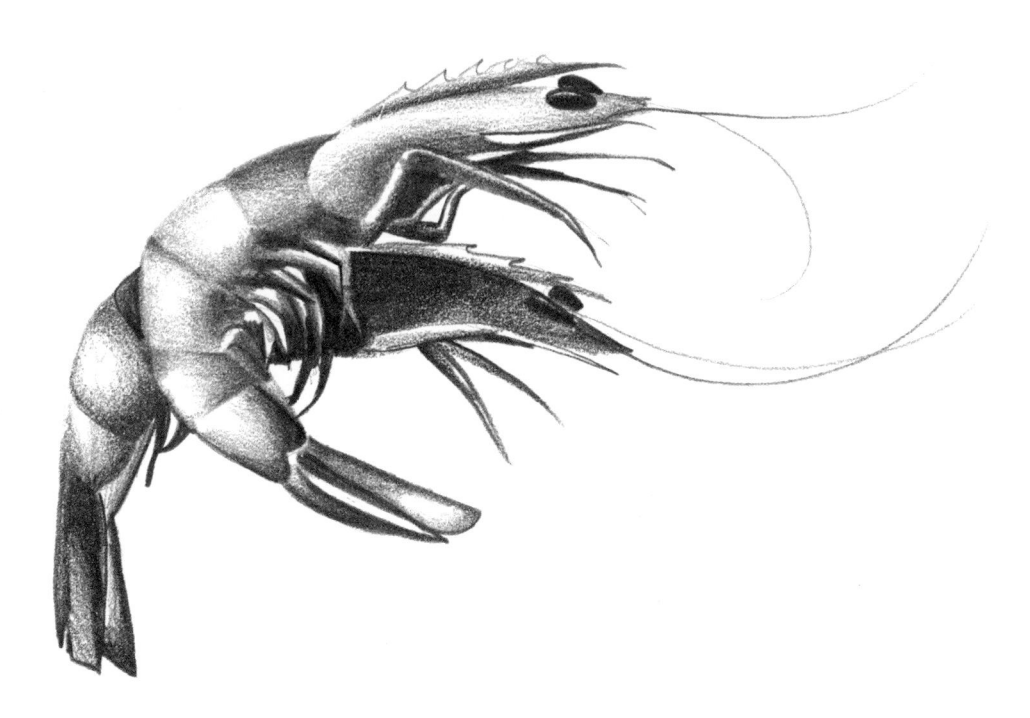

OILS

Fish · Souvlaki

This is a terrific dish to serve at a barbecue. If it is to be a "bush barbie" — carry the fish cubes and their marinade in a well sealed container and quickly prepare the dish on the spot. Although the quantity of oil is small, the mild fruitiness of the olives makes an important flavour contribution to this dish.

2 to 3 tablespoons virgin olive oil
1/3 cup (2 2/3 fl oz) dry white wine or dry vermouth
2 tablespoons white wine vinegar
2 teaspoons chopped fresh oregano, or 1 teaspoon dried oregano
2 garlic cloves, crushed
1/2 small white onion, grated or finely chopped

Black pepper
750 g (1 1/2 lb) firm-fleshed white fish fillets, cut into cubes about 5 x 5 x 2.5 cm (1 x 1 x 1 1/2 inch)
8 cherry tomatoes
8 button mushrooms
4 spring onions (scallions), cut into about 5 cm (2 inch) lengths
Wedges of lemon or lime
Fresh herb sprigs

Mix together the olive oil, wine, vinegar, oregano, garlic, chopped onion and pepper. Place the fish cubes in the marinade. Cover and chill for at least 8 hours.

Drain the fish and reserve the marinade. Thread the fish cubes onto well soaked wooden satay sticks, alternating with the tomato, mushroom and onion pieces.

Grill for 5 minutes on each side, brushing often with the reserved marinade.

Garnish with lemon wedges and herbs to serve. May be wrapped in pita bread for serving.

Serves 4

Prawn (Shrimps) · and · Watercress · Vinaigrette Platter

250 g (8 oz) cooked prawns (shrimps), shelled

3 tablespoons finely chopped celery

250 g (8 oz) cherry tomatoes, halved
Freshly ground pepper
½ cup (1 handful) watercress leaves
¼ cup (2 fl oz) virgin olive oil
1 tablespoon cider vinegar
1 garlic clove, finely chopped
1 mignonette (butterhead) lettuce, washed and crisped
30 g (1 oz) red caviar
3 hard-boiled eggs, shelled and quartered
16 stuffed olives, halved
Extra cress sprigs
1 cup lemon mayonnaise (see recipe, page 86)

Cut each cooked, shelled prawn into 3 pieces. Add the celery, tomatoes and pepper. Stir in cress leaves.

Mix together the oil, vinegar and garlic. Pour onto the prawn mixture and toss very lightly but thoroughly.

Arrange lettuce leaves on a large flat platter. Spoon prawn mixture onto the platter; top with caviar. Arrange the eggs and sliced olives alternately; garnish with watercress sprigs.

Serve with a separate bowl of lemon mayonnaise.

Serves 4 to 6

Marinated · Salmon

A friend who had eaten this dish in England gave me the recipe; she swears it is the best she has tasted anywhere. It certainly is excellent; just remember that you will need to start your preparations several days in advance of when you wish to serve the salmon.

1 kg (2 lb) coarse salt
3 cups (24 oz) sugar
1 teaspoon finely chopped dill
1 teaspoon finely chopped parsley
1 teaspoon finely chopped chervil
750 g (1½ lb) salmon fillet

Marinade
1½ cups (12 fl oz) dry riesling
½ cup (4 fl oz) extra-light olive oil

½ small white onion, finely chopped
1 teaspoon finely chopped dill
1 teaspoon finely chopped parsley
1 teaspoon finely chopped chervil
6 peppercorns, lightly crushed
1 bay leaf

Mix the salt, sugar, dill, parsley and chervil. Spread a layer in a glass casserole dish large enough to hold the salmon. Place salmon into the dish, cover with the remaining salt and sugar mixture. Cover tightly and refrigerate for 24 hours.

To make the marinade, combine the wine, oil, onion, herbs and peppercorns. Wipe the salt mixture from the salmon; place salmon into cold water for 5 minutes. Drain and pat it dry.

Return salmon to the washed glass dish, pour on the marinade. Cover tightly and refrigerate for 3 to 4 days. Remove salmon from the marinade and pat dry.

To serve, slice salmon very thinly across the grain. Serve with a few small lettuce leaves, water-thin slices of onion and a spoonful of home-made mayonnaise. Pass a peppermill.

Serves 8 to 10

Tuna · with · Beans

Typically Italian in flavour and presentation, this simple but delicious dish is an ideal choice for those occasions that call for interesting but effortless food.

250 g (8 oz) borlotti beans (pink Italian kidney beans; these are available in packets at most supermarkets or Italian delicatessens)
⅓ cup (2⅔ fl oz) virgin olive oil
375 g (12 oz) ripe, juicy tomatoes, seeded and chopped
2 red onions, thinly sliced
500 g (1 lb) tuna, drained and lightly flaked
Freshly ground pepper
2 tablespoons shredded basil

Garlic Vinaigrette

2 garlic cloves, halved
⅓ cup (2½ fl oz) virgin olive oil
1 tablespoon red wine vinegar (more or less, to taste)
½ teaspoon dry mustard
Salt (optional)
Plenty of coarsely ground black pepper

Soak the beans overnight; discard soaking water. Place the beans in a saucepan of cold water, bring to the boil and simmer gently until tender. (Follow directions on packet.) Drain well. Let cool to room temperature. Place the beans in a large bowl. Add the olive oil, tomatoes, onions, tuna, pepper, and basil.

To make the vinaigrette, place the garlic in a container that can be tightly covered. Add the olive oil and allow to stand overnight, tightly sealed. Next day, add the vinegar, mustard, salt, pepper and cover the container. Shake vigorously until well blended. The dressing may be strained or, if preferred, remove the garlic cloves before storing. (Flavour will intensify if garlic remains in the dressing.)

Pour dressing over salad and serve.

Serves 4

Beef · en · Daube

I love these robust country-style dishes, and to smell one of them simmering in the oven or on the stovetop takes me straight back to the south of France. This recipe is loosely based on one of Elizabeth David's classics, but is indeed just one of many, many similar — but different! — versions I have eaten over the years. I like to serve it with a pasta, and because I happen to love the flavour and textural combination of salad greens eaten with the wonderful juices left on the plate after a dish like this, I serve a simple green salad as well as plenty of bread and, of course, red wine.

2½ kg (3 lb) round of beef

Marinade

¼ cup (2 fl oz) virgin olive oil
1 white onion, sliced
2 shallots (scallions), chopped
1 celery stalk, sliced
1 carrot, chopped

OILS

Sprig of thyme	*1 bay leaf*
1 bay leaf	*1 large sprig parsley*
Sprig of oregano	*1 large sprig of thyme*
2 garlic cloves, slivered	*3 garlic cloves, slivered*
Few peppercorns	*4 slices lean bacon*
½ cup (4 fl oz) dry red wine	*185 g (6 oz) stoned black olives*
250 g (8 oz) carrots, cut into chunks	*3 large ripe tomatoes, peeled and chopped*

Trim excess fat from the meat and set aside.

To prepare the marinade, heat the oil in a small saucepan. Add the onion, shallots, celery and carrot. Simmer gently for several minutes. Add the herbs, garlic, peppercorns and red wine. Simmer gently for about 15 minutes. Allow to cool, then strain.

Place the meat in a bowl; pour on the marinade. Allow to stand for at least 12 hours, turning the meat several times to ensure it is well flavoured all over.

Next day, place the meat into a casserole into which it will fit neatly. Arrange the carrot pieces around the meat, add the fresh herbs and garlic. Place the bacon rashers on top of the meat; pour over the strained marinade.

Cover the pot tightly with greaseproof paper, put the lid in place. Cook in a low oven for about 2½ hours. Add the olives and tomatoes. Cook another 30 minutes and test for tenderness. Cut the bacon into squares, slice the meat thickly. Serve some of the wonderful pot juices with each portion.

Serves 8 to 10

Herbed · Chicken · and · Potato · Salad with · Avocado

This unusual salad is a delicious choice as the main course for a summer luncheon. Serve with a leafy green salad.

4 medium potatoes, unpeeled	*¼ cup (2 fl oz) white wine vinegar*
½ cup (4 fl oz) light olive oil	*4 chicken fillets, skin removed*

2 garlic cloves, lightly crushed	6 cherry tomatoes, halved or quartered
1 bay leaf	2 tablespoons lemon juice
1 sprig each of rosemary, thyme, parsley and sage	1 tablespoon finely chopped dill
3 spring onions (scallions), finely chopped, or 3 tablespoons chopped chives	Cayenne pepper
	2 avocadoes, peeled and sliced or cubed
2 tablespoons cress	Extra lemon juice

Cube the potatoes and simmer until just tender. Remove from liquid and drain potatoes.

Mix together the oil and vinegar, pour onto potatoes. Cover and chill for at least 8 hours. (This allows flavours to be absorbed.)

Place the chicken breasts into lightly salted water; add the garlic, bay leaf and herb sprigs. Cover and simmer until tender.

Remove the chicken, reserving the liquid; cut chicken into strips. Cover and set aside to cool. Strain the chicken stock and reserve 2 tablespoons; the remainder may be frozen for future use. Drain potatoes lightly. Toss with the chicken, spring onions, cress and tomatoes.

Mix together lemon juice, the reserved chicken stock, 2 tablespoons of dressing from potatoes, the dill and cayenne. Toss lightly.

Spoon onto serving platter and garnish with avocadoes, sprinkled with lemon juice. Serve at once.

Serves 4

Summer · Veal · Rolls · with · Basil

Fragrant with basil and garlic and topped with luscious sun-ripened tomatoes, this is a wonderful meal to serve for a casual dinner party. Serve it with little boiled potatoes and a large salad.

1.4 kg (3 lb) veal steaks (scallopine)	Seasoned flour
	¼ cup (2 fl oz) virgin olive oil

OILS

> 2 large onions, each cut
>   into 6 wedges
> 3 garlic cloves, chopped or
>   minced
> 1 cup (1½ oz) basil leaves,
>   finely shredded
> Salt
> Freshly ground black
>   pepper
> 8 medium-size very ripe
>   tomatoes, peeled
> ½ cup (4 fl oz) dry white
>   wine

Lightly pound the steaks unless quite thin. Cut into 2.5 cm (1 inch) strips crosswise. Roll up the slices, fasten with wooden toothpicks.

Lightly dredge the rolls in the seasoned flour. Heat the olive oil in a large pan and brown the rolls all over, about 3 minutes each side. Transfer rolls to a heavy, lidded saucepan.

Sauté the onions and garlic in the remaining oil until lightly coloured. Add to the veal in the saucepan.

Sprinkle half the chopped basil on top of the other ingredients; sprinkle with a little salt and pepper.

Cut the tomatoes into quarters and add to the saucepan; sprinkle on the remaining basil. Add the wine. Cover the saucepan and simmer over very low heat for about 1 hour, or until very tender.

Transfer the veal rolls, vegetables and juices to a serving platter. Remove the toothpicks and serve, garnished with fresh basil leaves.

Serves 8

Stewed · Okra

I ate this delicious dish in the Middle East, where okra is known by the name of "bamia". Frozen okra is fine for this recipe, if you can find it; otherwise, I suggest you blanch raw okra for increased tenderness.

> 1 kg (2 lb) frozen or fresh
>   okra
> 3 tablespoons olive oil
> 1 onion, finely chopped
> 3 cups (24 fl oz) tomato
>   purée (canned or home
>   prepared)
> 2 garlic cloves, very finely
>   chopped
> ½ teaspoon salt (optional)
> Freshly ground pepper

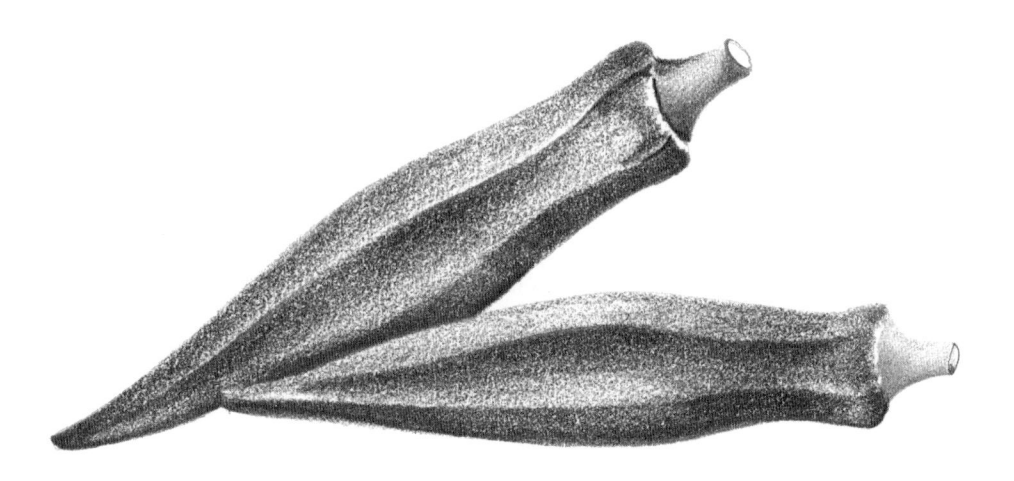

If okra is frozen, partially thaw it. If the fresh vegetable is used, bring a large saucepan of lightly salted water to a boil. Drop in the okra and boil for about 2 minutes. Drain and place under running cold water. Drain again.

Heat the oil in a nonreactive large saucepan. Sauté the onion until golden. Add the okra. Pour on the tomato purée; add the garlic and seasonings and mix well. Simmer gently for about 45 minutes, stirring occasionally. Check to ensure there is still sufficient liquid; if necessary, add a little water or tomato juice.

This dish may be served hot or cold, as a salad or side dish with chicken. We sometimes ate it as part of a spread of appetisers, when it was served with pita bread for scooping up the flavoursome sauce.

Serves 4 to 6

Truffa · D'Auvergne

This recipe was given to me after I had eaten (and loved) the dish in a tiny restaurant in France. I laboriously translated the recipe and it does seem to work almost as well to produce the results I enjoyed over there.

OILS

¼ cup (2 fl oz) light olive oil
500 g (1 lb) potatoes, peeled and very thinly sliced
200 g (7 oz) curd cream (cottage) cheese
Pepper

Heat the oil in a large skillet. Add the potato slices and cook for about 15 minutes, or until brown and crisp. Crumble the cheese into the potatoes, add the pepper and cook until the cheese melts.

This dish is often served only with wine and it was at a wine tasting that I first enjoyed it. I was told it is also served as an accompaniment to poached and grilled fish dishes. I usually serve it at lunch with a large green salad. Crisp grilled rashers of bacon offers a tasty, if not traditional, flavour addition.

Serves 4

Confit · of · Onions

The long and gentle cooking method used by the French to preserve goose or duck meat is called confit. However, although this is the same method, we use onions in this recipe and the end result is rather like an incredibly delicious and tender chutney. Serve the onion confit warm with hot pork or poultry or at room temperature with almost any cold meat.

500 g (1 lb) small pickling onions (the smaller the better)
1½ cups (12 fl oz) water
¼ cup (2 fl oz) extra-light olive oil
3 tablespoons wine vinegar (red or white)
3 tablespoons seeded raisins or sultanas
2 tablespoons light brown sugar
2 tablespoons tomato paste
5 garlic cloves, coarsely chopped
Salt (optional)
Freshly ground pepper
⅓ teaspoon ground cloves

Peel the onions; cut a shallow slit in the root end of each. Drop into boiling water and cook for 1 minute. Drain well and refresh under cold running water. Place all of the remaining ingredients into a large, heavy based, non-reactive saucepan. Stir until mixed. Add the onions. Cover tightly and cook very gently for about 1 hour.

Remove the lid, stir gently and simmer until the mixture is glossy and the onions are very tender, about 30 minutes. Stir occasionally to prevent sticking and burning.

Serve warm or if prepared in advance, store in the refrigerator in a covered container. The confit may be prepared up to 5 days ahead.

Serves 4 to 6

Leeks · with · Olive · Oil · and · Tomatoes

This recipe uses the superb extra-virgin olive oil that endows every dish with luscious flavour.

8 small young leeks
¼ cup (2 fl oz) extra-
virgin olive oil
Salt
Freshly ground black
pepper

500 g (1 lb) ripe tomatoes,
peeled and chopped
1 garlic clove, chopped
1 tablespoon finely
chopped parsley

Trim the leeks and wash thoroughly, with running water to remove any grit. Dry carefully.

Heat the oil in a large heavy pan. Arrange the leeks side by side in the pan. Sprinkle with salt and pepper. Cover the pan and cook the leeks over very low heat for 20 to 25 minutes, carefully turning them once.

Remove the leeks and arrange on a serving platter.

Add the tomatoes and garlic to the oil in the pan and cook for a few minutes. Stir in the parsley. Spoon the sauce over the leeks. Serve at room temperature.

Serves 4

OILS

Herbed · Slaw · with · Sprouts

A delightful variation on the more usual coleslaw; although less colourful, ordinary green cabbage may be substituted for the red.

1 small red cabbage
1½ cups (3 oz) mixed sprouts (bean, alfalfa, cress, etc.)
1 small red or white onion, very thinly sliced
½ cup (4 fl oz) light olive oil
¼ cup (2 fl oz) cider vinegar

1 tablespoon finely chopped fresh parsley
1½ teaspoons chopped fresh marjoram or oregano
Good pinch of cayenne pepper
3 tablespoons warm, toasted pine nuts

Shred the cabbage very finely and toss lightly with the sprouts and onion.

Combine the olive oil, vinegar, fresh herbs and cayenne and stir or shake well to make a dressing. Pour over cabbage mixture and toss lightly to mix.

Transfer to a serving bowl or platter, sprinkle with the warmed pine nuts and serve at once.

Serves 4

Tomatoes · with · Crisp · Crouton · Salad

5 cups (10 oz) Italian bread cubes
2 cups (32 whole) cherry tomatoes, halved

1 cup (3 oz) spring onions (scallions), chopped

Dressing

½ cup (4 fl oz) virgin olive oil

2 garlic cloves, crushed or finely chopped

OLIVE OIL

¼ cup (2 fl oz) red wine
    vinegar
1 tablespoon whole-grain
    mustard

Black pepper
Finely chopped basil

Place the bread cubes on a baking tray and toast for about 15 minutes at 180°C (360°F) until crisp and golden brown. Remove from the oven; allow to cool slightly. Place the croutons in a salad bowl; add the tomatoes and spring onions.

Combine all of the dressing ingredients in a jar and shake until well blended. Pour over the salad ingredients and toss very gently.

To ensure a crunchy texture, serve at once, sprinkled generously with basil.

Serves 6 to 8

A · Vegetarian · Salad · Delight

This delectable salad may be served as a first course or as a light main course. The combination of crunchy and tender textures plays an important role in this dish.

2 cups small, mixed lettuce
and other green leaves
(include if possible
lamb's lettuce (mâche),
witlof, rocket, cress, baby
spinach leaves)
12 asparagus spears,
    trimmed
⅓ cup (1½ oz) chopped
    canned water chestnuts

6 red or yellow miniature
    tomatoes, halved
6 abalone (oyster)
    mushrooms, cut into
    thick slices
1 large sweet orange,
    peeled and segmented

Olive Oil Dressing

¼ cup (2 fl oz) extra-
    virgin olive oil
1 tablespoon lemon juice
    (more or less, to taste)

Grated lemon zest
Pepper

Prepare the baby greens by rinsing lightly and drying well. Cook the asparagus in boiling water; drain and refresh under running water. Set aside.

Arrange the greens on platters, add the asparagus spears, water chestnuts, tomatoes, mushrooms and orange segments.

Make the dressing by whisking together all of the ingredients. Drizzle required amount over the salad; serve at once. If extra "crunch" is desired, add toasted, skinned almonds or hazelnuts to the salad ingredients.

Serves 2

NOTE: Any leftover dressing may be stored in a covered container in the refrigerator.

Multi-capsicum (Bell Pepper) · Salad

Looks great and tastes fantastic! The combination of the expensive and assertive walnut oil with a light olive oil offers an excellent contrast to the distinctive flavour of ripe capsicum (bell pepper).

1 small green capsicum (bell pepper)
1 small red capsicum (bell pepper)
1 small yellow capsicum (bell pepper)
2 celery stalks, finely sliced
90 g (3 oz) coarsely chopped toasted walnuts
1 cup (1½ oz) watercress sprigs

Sea salt (optional)
Freshly ground pepper
¼ cup (2 fl oz) extra-light olive oil
1 tablespoon walnut oil
Juice of 1 lemon
1 teaspoon grated lemon zest

Seed and core the capsicums; slice into rings. Arrange around the edge of an attractive serving platter.

Mix together the celery, nuts and watercress sprigs. Pile into the centre of the capsicum rings.

Sprinkle with salt and pepper. Combine the oils and lemon juice. Drizzle over the salad and serve at once.

Serves 4

Cold · Herbed · Tomato · Sauce

This delicious sauce is splendid served with chicken and fairly robust fish.

1 large can (450 g; 14½ oz) peeled tomatoes, chopped
1 tablespoon prepared mustard
¼ cup (4 fl oz) virgin olive oil
1 teaspoon finely chopped or grated shallots
(scallions — if unavailable, substitute white onion)
2 teaspoons assorted fresh herbs, such as chervil, tarragon, thyme, parsley
2 teaspoons white wine vinegar
Black pepper

Simmer the tomatoes and their juice over low heat until most of the juice evaporates.

Mash the tomatoes with a wooden spoon and continue simmering until reduced to the consistency of a thick, coarse purée. Set aside to cool.

Stir the mustard into the tomatoes; stir in the oil as for a mayonnaise (see recipe, *page 86*).

Add the shallots, herbs, vinegar and pepper to taste. May be covered and chilled until required.

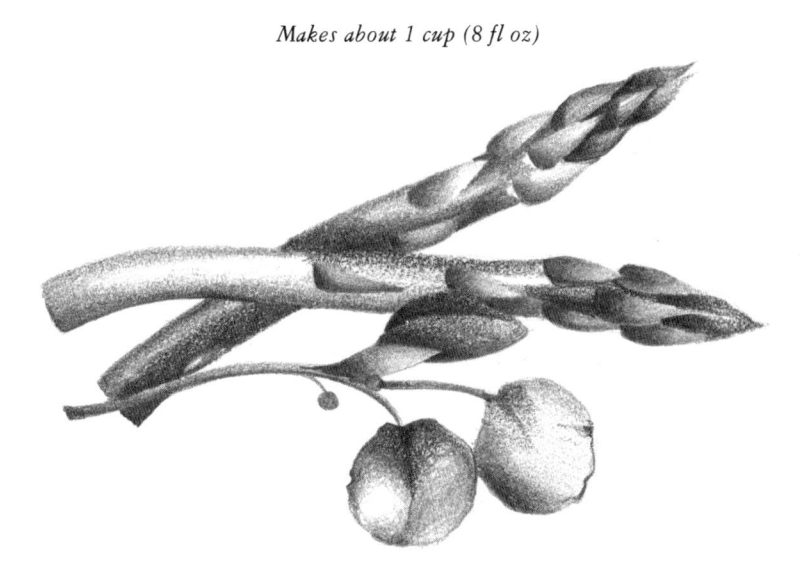

Makes about 1 cup (8 fl oz)

OILS

Parsley · Garlic · and · Tuna · Sauce

Certainly not the traditional pesto — no basil! — but this robust sauce is excellent served with pasta.

2 garlic cloves, chopped
2 cups (3 oz) firmly packed parsley sprigs
⅓ cup (1½ oz) pine nuts
½ cup (4 fl oz) virgin olive oil

3 tablespoons freshly grated Parmesan cheese
1 can (225 g; 7½ oz) tuna, drained and finely flaked

Place the garlic, parsley and pine nuts in the bowl of a food processor or blender. Process for about 30 seconds using the on/off switch on the machine. With the motor running, gradually pour in the olive oil. Purée until smooth. Add the cheese and process for 15 seconds.

Stir in the flaked tuna and mix thoroughly.

Toss through hot cooked pasta — serve extra coarsely grated Parmesan cheese separately. As a change, serve this pasta sauce, tossed through cold, wholemeal spiral pasta to create an interesting salad.

Serves 4

Preserved · Basil

Of all the herbs of summer, it is the fresh basil I miss most when the first cold days of autumn wither the leaves on the bush. However, by using this method of preservation it is possible to retain the fresh flavour of this lovely herb for months. It also provides a fragrant oil to use as the basis for dressings. Choose fresh basil leaves in good condition and pick them when they are dry; otherwise, rinse them and dry well.

4 cups (4 oz) basil leaves
½ cup (4 fl oz) light olive oil

Additional olive oil

Place 2 handfuls of the leaves in a blender or food processor with the ½ cup (4 fl oz) of olive oil. Chop to a fine consistency but do not purée. Add the remaining leaves in handful increments and process, scraping down the sides of the bowl as necessary.

Spoon the basil and oil mixture into a ceramic or glass container. Pour on sufficient additional oil to cover the basil mixture by about 2.5 cm (1 inch). Cover the container and refrigerate until required.

To use the basil in recipes calling for fresh basil, spoon out the amount needed and drain the oil back into the container. Add a little more fresh olive oil each time. This basil will keep for several months.

Makes about 1 cup (8 oz)

An · Excellent · Batter · (1)

It is difficult to find a really versatile batter recipe, but I find this a very satisfactory one for most purposes. For sweet batters, a dash of rum adds interest. Most batter mixtures improve if allowed to stand for a while — this one is no exception.

250 g (8 oz) plain (all-purpose) flour
2 eggs
¼ cup (2 fl oz) extra-light olive oil
6 tablespoons (3 fl oz) milk
Salt (optional)
1 tablespoon brandy

Sift the flour into a bowl. Separate the eggs. Beat together egg yolks, oil, milk, salt and brandy.

Make a well in the centre of the flour, pour in the liquid and blend in until it is quite smooth. Allow to stand for at least 30 minutes. Just before using the batter, beat the egg white stiffly, then lightly fold into the mixture.

NOTE: ½ teaspoon of baking powder sifted with the flour will lighten the batter.

An · Excellent · Batter · (2)

This slightly different version gives a very light crisp finish to the batter; it is excellent for fish fillets.

250 g (8 oz) plain (all-purpose) flour
2 eggs, well beaten
Salt
Foaming beer (1 can)

Sift the flour; stir in the eggs and salt. Add sufficient beer to make a light and frothy batter. Set aside for about 30 minutes. Stir lightly before using the batter.

Black · and · Green · Olive · Bread

You'll think you're in Italy when you taste this wonderful fragrant bread. Enjoy!

4 cups (16 oz) plain (all-purpose) flour
1½ envelopes (10 g; 4 oz) of "instant" dry yeast
1 cup (5 oz) stuffed olives, chopped
1 cup (5 oz) black olives, stoned and chopped
¼ cup (2 fl oz) extra-light olive oil, heated to lukewarm
½ cup (4 fl oz) water, heated to lukewarm
¼ cup (2 fl oz) milk, heated to lukewarm
Black pepper
Milk, for glaze

In a large bowl, mix together all of the ingredients. Stir well. Turn onto a floured board and knead for several minutes until the dough is shiny and elastic to the touch.

Place dough back into a clean bowl, cover with plastic wrap and stand in a warm spot for about 50 minutes, or until dough has doubled in size.

Punch down the dough and knead for about 5 minutes; shape dough into one large or two smaller loaves. Place onto a greased baking tray and return to rise in a warm place for about 40 minutes. Brush with milk. Bake at 200°C (400°F) for 30 minutes, or until bread is golden in colour and crust sounds hollow when rapped with the knuckles.

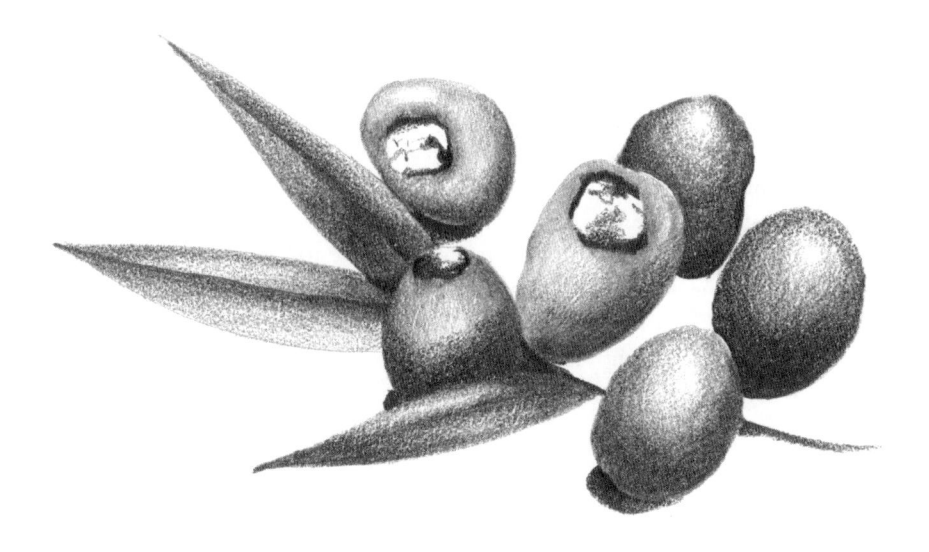

Turkish · Flatbread

Although the basic dough is the same, I was told by friends from the Middle East that the shape of this bread varies from region to region. Sometimes shaped into sheets 75 cm (30 inches) by 30 cm (12 inches), it may also be baked as a flat, round loaf about 20 cm (8 inches) in diameter. Sometimes, too, the outer edges are turned up to form a rim, and the center is filled with feta cheese or spiced beef.

15 g (½ oz) compressed yeast
150 ml (½ cup) lukewarm water
250 g (8 oz) plain (all-purpose) flour
2 teaspoons salt
5 tablespoons (2½ fl oz) light olive oil
1 tablespoon sesame seeds
2 tablespoons melted unsalted butter
Beaten egg

Blend the yeast with a little of the warm water in a small bowl. In a large bowl, stir together the flour, salt and oil until thoroughly mixed. Add the yeast mixture, then gradually add most of the rest of the water. The mixture should form a soft dough, without being sticky, so do not add the remaining water unless necessary. Turn it onto a lightly floured board and knead for about 10 minutes, or until the dough is satiny and elastic to the touch.

OILS

Place the dough in a lightly oiled bowl, cover with a tea-towel and leave in a warm spot to rise for about 30 minutes.

Knead again for several minutes. Divide the dough into 2 or 3 portions. Shape each piece into a ball, then roll each into a round of about 20 cm (8 inches) diameter. Place onto lightly oiled baking trays and sprinkle with sesame seeds.

Using finger tips, make a number of indentations in the surface of the dough and place trays into a very hot oven (200°C to 250°C/450°F to 500°F) for 5 minutes. After that time, remove the bread from the oven, brush first with the melted butter then the beaten egg. Bake for another 10 minutes, or until golden brown. This bread is usually torn rather than cut into serving pieces.

Nut Oils

Nut oils are expensive but a little of their rich nutty flavour goes a long way.

Carefully selected nuts are crushed in a mill then heated until they form a golden-brown paste. This roasting gives the oil its flavour and aroma. During heating they are constantly stirred to prevent burning, as the free oil runs off. The paste is then spread on mats and subjected to hydraulic pressure to extract the rest of the oil. The free-run oil and the pressed oil are then mixed before filtering and bottling.

WALNUT OIL

Walnut oil is a polyunsaturated oil with a rich full flavour, distinctly reminiscent of the nut from which it comes. It is made from nuts that are dried (roasted) and cold pressed; walnut oil extracted under heat is not edible. Although unroasted walnut oil has been made for centuries, walnut oil has been in culinary use only since the 19th century. Unroasted oil is used in cosmetics and to preserve wood — in the past it was made into varnish and used, for instance, on Stradivarius violins.

The main use for walnut oil is in salads. Like other nut oils, it's not suitable for deep-frying, but you can use it to baste meats when grilling or roasting, and to flavour stir-fried vegetables. I like to add it to walnut bread as shortening and brush it over the loaf when it's cooked.

OILS

The United States is the world's largest producer of walnuts, but the best walnut oils are made in France. The best oil comes from the best nuts, and the best nuts are grown in France's Dordogne region. There are many varieties and grades of walnut; the French will even classify nuts from the same tree in two different grades according to colour and taste.

Walnut oil is affected by light and exposure to air and should be kept in a tin in a cool place. However, it will go slightly cloudy if stored in the refrigerator.

Gourmet · Pizza

This very glamorous version of the simple pizza has a base rather like focaccia bread, thick and chewy. It is delicious combined with the earthy flavours of walnut oil, Parmesan cheese and sun-dried tomatoes.

Dough Base

- 60 g (2 oz) compressed yeast or 30 g (1 oz) granular yeast
- 500 to 600 ml (12 to 16 fl oz) lukewarm water
- ¼ cup (2 fl oz) walnut oil
- Salt
- 1 kg (2¼ lb) plain (all-purpose) flour

Topping

- 2 tablespoons oil from the sun-dried tomatoes
- 60 g (2 oz) sun-dried tomatoes in oil, drained and coarsely chopped
- 60 g (2 oz) Parmesan cheese, coarsely grated
- 90 g (3 oz) pitted black olives (preferably Calamata or Niçoise)
- 2 tablespoons finely chopped oregano or marjoram
- 1 tablespoon finely chopped Italian parsley
- 1 teaspoon coarse sea salt
- 2 tablespoons walnut oil
- Black pepper
- 2 tablespoons Italian parsley leaves
- Extra shredded or grated Parmesan

NUT OILS

Garnish
Small bunches of marjoram or oregano

To make the dough, dissolve the yeast in a bowl with a little of the water. Add the walnut oil and salt. Sift the flour into a large bowl, make a well in the centre and pour in the yeast mixture. Mix to form a dough, adding more water if necessary. Knead until smooth and elastic to the touch. Cover and set aside in a warm place until double in size, probably about 1 hour. Roll out lightly to form a round of dough about ¾ inch thick. Place the dough circle onto a lightly oiled baking tray and brush with the oil from the tomatoes. Arrange the tomatoes, Parmesan, olives, herbs, salt and pepper on top. Sprinkle on the walnut oil. Bake for 25 to 30 minutes, or until golden brown. Top with Italian parsley leaves and Parmesan. Garnish with fresh herbs. Serve broken into large pieces.

Serves 6

"Fast · Food" · Gourmet · Chicken

Have you ever had the experience of recklessly inviting someone for an impromptu meal and then realising that your cupboards are bare? It is a good idea to keep a few interesting ingredients tucked away on your pantry shelves — a selection of good oils and vinegars are truly essential — and with a few quick purchases on the way home, you can arrive almost as your guest does and still be able to present a palatable meal. This recipe relies on the readily available barbecued chicken from your local take-away.

1 large barbecued chicken, cut into slices and bite-size portions
4 Lebanese cucumbers or 1 small Continental cucumber
6 canned artichoke hearts
1 large apple, unpeeled, but cored and sliced
1 celery stalk, thinly sliced diagonally
2 spring onions (scallions), cut lengthwise into strips
90 g (3 oz) lightly toasted pecans, coarsely chopped
Radicchio leaves or similar exotic salad leaves

OILS

Dressing

2 tablespoons walnut oil
2 tablespoons peanut oil
1 tablespoon lemon juice
or cider vinegar
2 teaspoons finely chopped
mint (mint sauce will do)

$1/3$ teaspoon sugar
Salt (optional)
Pepper

Prepare the chicken, discarding the chicken skin if preferred. Cut the cucumbers very thinly lengthwise; cut the drained artichoke hearts into quarters. Mix chicken, cucumber strips, artichokes, apple, celery, onions and pecans; toss lightly.

Arrange the salad leaves attractively on individual plates. Spoon on the salad. Whisk together the dressing ingredients and drizzle over the salad. Garnish with fresh mint leaves if available, or any other attractive edible leaf such as geranium, nasturtium, etc.

Serves 6

Pasta · Salad · with · Walnuts

The blandness of pasta provides a perfect background for the rich and varied flavours of this cheese and walnut sauce which caps it. Add additional texture and flavour by serving it with a crisp salad of mixed greens.

    250 g (9 oz) mixed green, white and orange coloured pasta
    1 tablespoon walnut oil
    90 g (3 oz) blue cheese, at room temperature
    ¼ cup (2 fl oz) light cream
    ½ cup (4 fl oz) cultured sour cream
    Sea salt (optional)
    Lemon juice
    ½ cup (2 oz) chopped lightly toasted walnuts or pecans
    Freshly ground pepper or seasoned pepper

Cook pasta in lightly salted water until al dente. Drain well and toss with the walnut oil. Set aside to cool.

    Mash the cheese, add the cream and sour cream and whisk until smooth. Add the salt (if using) and the lemon juice. Pour onto the noodles. Add the walnuts and pepper and toss through the noodles.

    Pile onto a large serving platter. Serve with a crisp salad that includes some bitter greens such as witlof (Belgian endive), rocket (aragula) or chicory.

Serves 4 to 6

Smoked · Chicken · with · Poached · Pear and · Walnut · Salad

This salad is equally delicious if gipsy ham (double smoked ham) is substituted for the chicken — even better with smoked game birds, if you have access to them!

    3 pears, peeled, cored and quartered
    2 tablespoons castor (granulated) sugar
    1 tablespoon lemon juice
    ⅓ cup (1 oz) toasted walnuts, coarsely chopped
    4 smoked chicken breasts (or other smoked meats)
    1½ cups (3 oz) mixed salad greens, well washed and crisped

Walnut Vinaigrette

1 tablespoon Dijon mustard	Pepper
1 egg yolk	½ cup (4 fl oz) walnut oil
2 tablespoons red wine vinegar	½ cup (4 fl oz) extra-light olive oil

Prepare pears. Combine enough water to cover the pears with the sugar in a pan. Stir well and simmer over moderate heat, stirring occasionally until the sugar dissolves. Add the lemon juice.

Place the pear quarters into the syrup. Poach for 10 to 15 minutes, or until barely tender. Remove from syrup; drain and cool.

While the pears cook, toast the walnuts in a 200°C (400°F) oven for about 10 minutes, turning occasionally.

Remove and discard the skin from chicken breasts. Cut the meat into neat slivers. Arrange the sliced chicken and pear slices alternately on a serving plate. Garnish with the mixed greens. To make the dressing, whisk the mustard into the egg yolk. Add the vinegar and pepper to taste. Gradually whisk in the combined oils. Drizzle the vinaigrette over the chicken and pear salad; sprinkle on the toasted walnuts. Serve at once.

Serves 6

NOTE: If a stronger walnut flavour is preferred, increase the proportion of walnut oil to ¾ cup (6 fl oz) and reduce the olive oil proportionately.

Green · Salad · with · Toasted · Pecans

This simple but very beautiful salad's appeal depends on the combination of flavours offered by the warm pecans and the richness of the walnut oil in the dressing.

Variety of green, red and variegated lettuce leaves (equivalent of 2 lettuces)	wine vinegar (little more or less, to taste)
½ cup (4 fl oz) walnut oil	Salt
1 tablespoon white or red	Freshly ground pepper
	90 g (3 oz) toasted pecans

NUT OILS

Prepare the greens by washing, drying thoroughly and crisping in a covered container or loosely tied plastic bag.

Make the dressing by combining the oil, vinegar and salt and pepper and shaking well or whisking together. This may be made up in advance and covered and chilled until required, but allow it to come back to room temperature before serving.

Arrange the greens in a serving bowl. Roast or toast the pecans until very lightly browned, allow to cool until they are just warm. Break them into pieces (not too small); toss with the lettuces.

Pour on a little dressing, toss and serve at once. I like to pass extra dressing separately for those who like to indulge! It is also a good idea to serve a good light rye bread with this salad — perfect for mopping up those delectable juices!

Serves 4 to 6

NOTE: Walnuts may be substituted for the pecans — I happen to have a penchant for the pecan. Hazelnut oil and toasted hazelnuts may also be used. I find it a bit too powerful alone, so usually mix it with half extra-light olive oil or grapeseed oil.

A · Healthy · but · Delicious · Rice · Salad

Yes, I know brown rice salad can be pretty boring, but not this one! It tastes so good you won't believe it's healthy.

2 cups (8 oz) cooked brown rice
5 tablespoons extra-light olive oil
3 tablespoons walnut oil
2 tablespoons lemon juice
1 garlic clove, finely chopped
60 g (2 oz) toasted walnuts or pecans, coarsely chopped
2 tablespoons small cress leaves
2 tablespoons toasted sunflower seeds
1 tablespoon finely chopped chives
1 tablespoon finely chopped mint
1 tablespoon finely chopped parsley

OILS

Drain rice well and set aside.

Mix together olive oil, walnut oil, lemon juice and garlic. Pour over warm rice. Toss well and allow to cool. Toss in remaining ingredients. Chill slightly before serving.

Serves 4

Walnut · Oil · Vinaigrette

¾ cup (6 fl oz) walnut oil
1 tablespoon lemon juice
1 teaspoon Dijon mustard
Salt (optional)
Freshly ground pepper

Combine all of the ingredients in a screw top jar and shake well to blend. Store in refrigerator. If oil solidifies, allow to stand at room temperature until it regains its clarity.

Herbed · Raspberry · Vinegar · Dressing

¼ cup (2 fl oz) raspberry vinegar
⅓ cup (2⅔ fl oz) walnut oil
⅓ cup (2⅔ fl oz) peanut oil
2 teaspoons finely chopped fresh tarragon
2 teaspoons finely chopped fresh chervil
2 teaspoons finely chopped fresh chives
Pinch of salt
Freshly ground black pepper

Combine all of the ingredients in a jar; shake vigorously until blended.

Walnut · Bread

There are plenty of recipes for walnut bread, and many of them are delicious. After experimenting with several variations, this one is my favourite now. I like to serve it with cheese or salads. It freezes well and keeps fresh in an airtight container for several days. It toasts beautifully and is great to serve with soups.

500 g (1 lb) wholemeal flour
500 g (1 lb) plain white (all-purpose) flour
1 teaspoon salt
30 g (1 oz) compressed yeast or 15 g (½ oz) granulated yeast
1 tablespoon molasses, treacle or honey
500 ml (about 16 fl oz) lukewarm water
2 tablespoons walnut oil
¾ cup (3 oz) coarsely chopped walnuts

Combine the flours and salt in a large bowl. In another bowl blend together the yeast and molasses. Gradually add the water and stir together. Set aside in a warm place until the mixture begins to froth.

When the mixture is "working", make a well in the center of the flour and pour in the liquid; pour the walnut oil on top. Using a wooden spoon, mix together and add the walnuts. When the dough is mixed, knead on a lightly floured board until smooth. (Dip hands into flour if mixture is sticky or add a little more flour to the dough.)

When the dough is pliable and not sticky, place it in a lightly oiled bowl; cover with a cloth and set in a warm place until doubled in size.

Divide the dough in half. Shape each half into a loaf. Place each loaf in a loaf pan oiled with walnut oil. Allow to rise again until the dough is level or slightly above the rim of the tins. Place into a preheated 200°C (400°F) oven and bake for 10 minutes. Reduce the heat to 190°C (375°F) and continue baking for another 40 minutes. Remove loaves from the oven; cool on a wire rack.

Makes 2 loaves

NOTE: If a glossy surface is preferred, brush the loaves with a mixture of egg yolk and a little water about 10 minutes before completion of cooking time.

Hazelnut Oil

Hazelnut is a monounsaturated oil that was first produced commercially in 1978. It has the scent of fresh hazelnuts and a subtle flavour, which is more delicate than walnut oil. It's also more expensive than walnut oil because the nuts contain a lower percentage of oil.

It's not suitable for deep-frying and the flavour deteriorates if it's heated too much, so its main use is in salad dressing. For a special treat, sauté chicken breasts in a little hazelnut oil, then deglaze the pan with a dash of Cognac, add a little cream, salt and pepper. Spoon over the chicken and garnish with toasted hazelnuts. Or before baking bread or a cake, try brushing the tin with hazelnut oil for a wonderful flavour and aroma.

France is the main producer of hazelnut oil from hazelnuts that are grown in France, Italy and Turkey.

The oil can go rancid and is affected by light, so buy it in small quantities and store it in a tin in a cool place.

Salad · of · Baby · Greens · with Pâté · on · Hazelnut · Croutons

This delicate entrée provides a delightful springtime taste of the first asparagus of the season.

Croutons
4 thin slices wholemeal bread
Hazelnut oil

Salad
3 cups (6 oz) young greens such as baby endive, witlof (endive), lettuce leaves, rocket (aragula), watercress, etc.
12 stalks fresh asparagus
1 celery heart

Dressing

¼ cup (2 fl oz) hazelnut oil
2 teaspoons white wine
   vinegar
Salt (optional)
Freshly ground pepper
90 g (3 oz) high-quality pâté
   (either homemade or
   commercially prepared)

To make the croutons, remove the crusts from the bread and cut into 2.5 cm (1 inch) squares, using a fancy metal cutter. Brush each crouton on both sides with hazelnut oil. Place on a baking sheet and bake on the centre of a preheated 180°C (350°F) oven for about 12 minutes, or until croutons are crisp and golden. Cool and store in an airtight container until required.

Lightly rinse and dry the greens. Place in a plastic lettuce crisper or plastic bag and chill until needed. Break off the coarse stem ends of asparagus. Lightly cook in boiling water for only 5 minutes; refresh under running cold water. Cover and set aside. Cut the celery heart into fine julienne.

To prepare the dressing, combine all ingredients in a jar and shake until well mixed. To assemble the dish, arrange heaps of the mixed greens on small serving plates, place asparagus tips and celery julienne on top. Spread the pâté onto the cold or warm croutons (much nicer if they are still slightly warm). Sprinkle on a little more pepper. Drizzle on the preferred amount of dressing. Arrange the croutons on the salad and serve at once.

Serves 4 to 6

A · Salad · for · Autumn

Use the spoils of autumn to create this delightful salad to serve with grilled (broiled) chicken or quail.

6 French sorrel leaves
6 small spinach leaves
1 cup (2 oz) mesclun
   (mixed baby greens)
16 champignons, halved
4 abalone (oyster)
   mushrooms, cut into strips
1 red capsicum (bell
   pepper) halved, seeded
   and roasted
1 teaspoon very finely
   chopped chives
Freshly ground pepper

OILS

Hazelnut Oil Vinaigrette

½ cup (4 fl oz) hazelnut oil
1 tablespoon red wine vinegar
1 teaspoon balsamic vinegar
Pinch of salt
Freshly ground pepper
½ cup (2 oz) warm, lightly toasted and skinned hazelnuts, coarsely chopped, for garnish.

Arrange sorrel and spinach leaves and the mesclun on a serving platter. Prepare champignons and abalone mushrooms; cut the roasted capsicums into strips and arrange on the platter. Sprinkle on the chives and pepper.

To make the Hazelnut Oil Vinaigrette, combine the oil, vinegars and salt and pepper. Shake or whisk vigorously. Sprinkle the warm chopped hazelnuts on top of the salad, drizzle the dressing over the salad and serve immediately. Store any unused vinaigrette in a tightly covered container in the refrigerator.

NUT OILS

Wild · Rice · Salad · with · Hazelnut · Oil Dressing

Wild rice has become a popular gourmet item in recent years and offers a pleasantly nutty flavour that is enhanced by the addition of the hazelnuts. Although actually a grass seed, wild rice is cooked in the same way as brown rice; do not overcook it.

2¼ cups (11 oz) uncooked wild rice
½ cup (1 handful) very finely chopped parsley
½ cup (8 whole) halved baby yellow pear tomatoes or cherry tomatoes
Freshly ground black pepper

Hazelnut Oil Dressing

3 tablespoons hazelnut oil
1 tablespoon extra-light olive oil
1 tablespoon white wine vinegar
Salt (optional)
Plenty of freshly ground pepper
1 cup (4 oz) toasted hazelnuts, coarsely chopped

Cook the rice in lightly salted boiling water (as for white rice) until it is tender, about 30 to 35 minutes. Drain well and set aside to cool completely. Place the wild rice in a large bowl; stir in the parsley. Stir in the tomatoes and pepper. Mix lightly but thoroughly.

To make the Hazelnut Oil Dressing, combine the oils and vinegar in a jar and shake well. Season to taste with salt and pepper. Pour over the rice and mix again very lightly. Allow to stand for at least 1 hour; this gives the rice time to absorb the delicious dressing and juices and to become plump and succulent.

At serving time, add the toasted hazelnuts and serve at once.

Serves 6

Salad · of · Brown · Rice · and · Nuts

I love the crunchiness of this healthy summer salad and serve it often. Decorate it with colourful nasturtium flowers and leaves — and don't forget that they are edible as well as pretty. This salad is best made just before serving time; otherwise the nuts lose their crunchiness.

3 cups (12 oz) cooked brown rice
4 spring onions (scallions), finely chopped
1 celery stalk, thinly sliced diagonally
1 cup (4 oz) roasted nuts (peanuts, cashews, hazelnuts — mixed or just one variety), very coarsely chopped
Finely grated zest of 1 orange
1 tablespoon finely chopped parsley

Dressing

⅓ (2⅔ fl oz) cup hazelnut oil
⅓ (2⅔ fl oz) cup extra-light olive oil
1 to 2 tablespoons white wine vinegar
½ teaspoon dry mustard
Pinch of sugar
Pinch of salt
Freshly ground black pepper
Nasturtium flowers and small leaves of the plant, for garnish

Combine the rice and all of the other ingredients for the salad.

To make the dressing, combine all of the ingredients and whisk or shake vigorously in a covered container until well blended. Spoon required amount over the salad and toss lightly until well mixed. (Leftover dressing may be stored in the refrigerator.)

Spoon the salad onto an attractive serving platter. Garnish with a sprinkle of flower petals, tuck a few whole flowers with a couple of leaves to one side of the platter and serve at once.

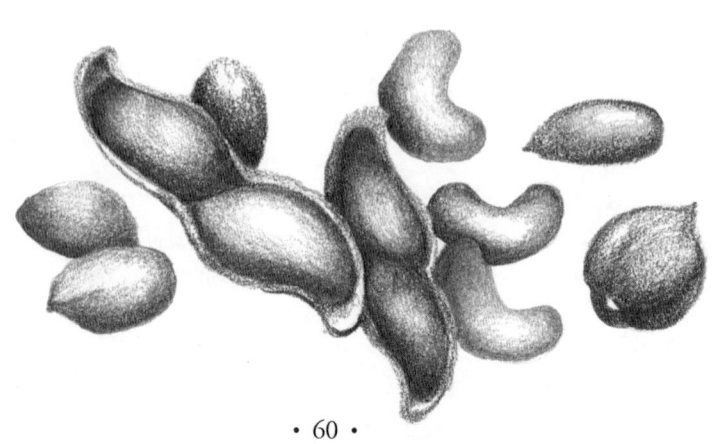

Serves 4

Almond Oil

Almond oil is a monounsaturated oil first produced commercially in 1980. It has a delicate, fresh almond flavour, a light consistency and a lovely amber colour.

It takes 3 kg (7 lb) of almonds to produce 1 l (40 fl oz) of oil (compared with 2 kg (4.5 lb) of walnuts and 2.5 kg (5.5 lb) of hazelnuts), so it is expensive. Use it to brush baking trays for meringues or molds for chocolate. It's also delicious brushed on fish while grilling (broiling), or used in a vinaigrette dressing for avocadoes. Or use it to sauté flaked almonds to toss over beans or broccoli.

Almond oil is made mainly in France from almonds grown in Spain. Don't confuse it with *amande douce*, which is made from almonds, but without heat to extract the flavour and aroma. This is sometimes labelled "almond oil" and is used mainly in the cosmetics industry.

Pistachio Oil

Pistachio is a new monounsaturated oil, first produced in 1988. It has a strong green colour and a distinctive flavour and smell. It is little used in cooking.

Vegetable Oils

Almost every part of the world has some sort of oil-producing plant crop.

Oil extraction from plant seeds is more complex than extraction from olives or nuts. Seeds are cleaned, then broken by rollers. The cracked seeds are heated to burst the walls of the oil cells and then pressed to extract oil. Any remaining oil is then removed by solvent: The seed cake is broken up by rollers and soaked with solvent until most of the oil has dissolved. Heat is used to evaporate the solvent from the oil and the crude oil is then ready for refining.

The first stage of the refining process removes the acid formed by the early production process. An alkali is added and the mixture reacts to form a soap, which sinks to the bottom of the tank. The oil is then washed with hot water to remove the soap. The next step is to bleach the oil with an agent such as carbon or Fuller's earth. The resulting pale coloured oil is then filtered off, and the taste and smell is neutralized by passing steam through the hot oil in a vacuum. Some of the oil extracted by pressing is then added to the neutral oil for flavour and colour.

Most vegetable oils have a high smoking point and so are suitable for frying. And with a few exceptions, they are almost tasteless, which makes them useful in dishes where no additional flavour is required.

Fried · Quail · with · Chili · Sauce

The spicy flavours of Thai cuisine add great interest to this dish, but remember to treat those hot chilies with caution and to wash your hands well after touching them!

6 medium-size quail
1¼ cups (10 fl oz) vegetable oil
3 garlic cloves, finely chopped
3 small hot chilies, seeded and chopped
1½ tablespoons oyster sauce

3 tablespoons nam pla (fish sauce)
1½ tablespoons chili paste
⅓ cup (2½ fl oz) chicken stock
2 tablespoons chopped basil leaves

Wipe the quail, pat dry and cut in half lengthwise. Remove ribcage, using a sharp knife. Gently flatten each piece; halve crosswise.

Heat the oil in a wok and fry the quail portions until cooked through, about 8 minutes. Remove and set side.

Leaving about ¼ cup (2 fl oz) of oil in the wok, add the garlic and cook until golden. Add the quail portions, chilies, oyster sauce, *nam pla* and chili paste. Stir well. Add the chicken stock and stir-fry for a few minutes. Adjust seasoning as desired. Add the basil and stir through the mixture. Remove from the heat and serve over hot steamed rice.

Serves 6

NOTE: Chicken breasts may be substituted for quail, if desired.

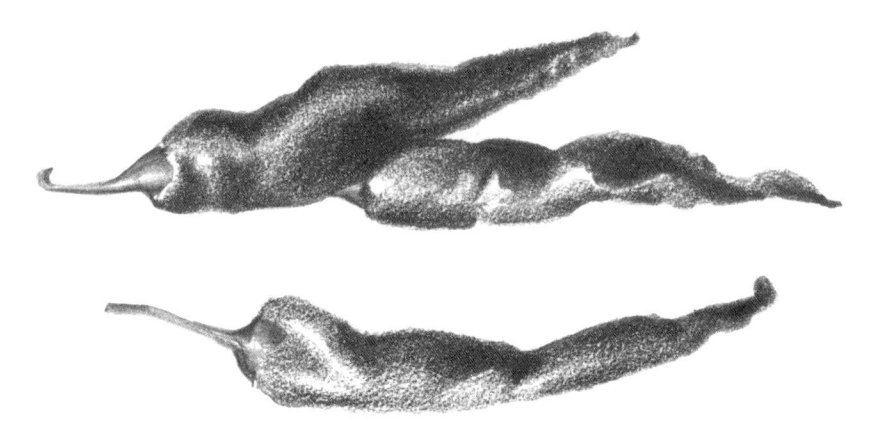

Coconut Oil

Coconut oil comes from the dried copra (white meat of the coconut). It contains natural lecithin, which helps prevent food from sticking to the pan and drops of water spattering, so it is an excellent frying oil. But the health-conscious may wish to avoid it because of its 90 percent saturated fatty acid content.

Avocado Oil

Producers in California have recently been promoting avocado oil as a relatively low-kilojoule oil. Mainly monounsaturated, it is produced without the addition of chemicals and has a slight aniseed flavour. Although its high smoking point (220°C/428°F) and high percentage of lecithin make it an excellent cooking oil, its price means that it would be wasteful to use it for deep-frying. Its unusual flavour is an interesting addition to salad dressings.

Sesame Oil

Oriental sesame oil is a key ingredient in Asian cookery. There are two types: one is a light yellowish colour, with a medium to strong flavour; the other, made with roasted sesame seeds, is dark brown and has an extremely strong flavour and aroma. A few drops of either transform the blandest food. The plant is probably of African origin, and most sesame oil is produced in the Middle East and Asia. Middle Eastern oils tend to be of the lighter variety, Asian of the stronger variety. In the United States both Oriental and non-oriental sesame oil are available. It is recommended that the stronger flavoured Oriental sesame oil, available from specialty stores and supermarkets, be used.

An unsaturated oil, sesame oil is used mainly in cooking, although you can try it sparingly in salad dressing. A little goes a long way. You can also use it instead of butter or margarine when cooking eggs; the rich, nutty flavour is particularly delicious with omelettes or scrambled eggs. And a few drops enliven a simple soup of chicken stock and noodles, or a dish of steamed green vegetables.

Wonton · Soup

This is a delicately flavoured soup, which may be served as a first course or as a light meal in itself.

500 g (1 lb) lean pork, finely chopped
2 cups (4 oz) finely shredded Chinese cabbage
1 tablespoon soy sauce
1 teaspoon grated fresh green ginger
1 teaspoon Oriental sesame oil

24 wonton wrappers (available in most Chinese delicatessen shops)
1 egg, lightly beaten
8 cups (64 fl oz) rich chicken stock
Spring onions (scallions), for garnish

Using a food processor or cleaver, very coarsely chop and blend together the pork and cabbage. Place in a bowl and add the soy sauce, ginger and ½ teaspoon of the sesame oil. Allow to marinate for at least 1 hour.

Wrap the pork mixture into the wontons so they form little pouches, moisten the outer edges of the wrappers with the beaten egg and seal firmly, pinching together with finger and thumb to ensure they adhere.

Bring the stock to a boil with the oil. Add the wontons and cook at a fast simmer for about 15 minutes, or until they pop to the surface.

Serve the stock with the wontons. Garnish with some finely shredded spring onions (scallions) before serving.

Serves 4 to 6

Spiced · Seafood · Salad

The combination of ingredients in this dish evokes a sense of Asia and offers an interesting flavour sensation. The dressing may be made well in advance and stored in the refrigerator.

500 g (1 lb) firm-fleshed boneless fish fillets

⅓ cup (2⅔ fl oz) lemon juice

SESAME OIL

2 teaspoons peanut oil
1 teaspoon Oriental
  sesame oil

15 g (½ oz) fresh green
  ginger slivered

Salad

1 red capsicum (bell
  pepper), seeded and
  deribbed
½ Chinese cabbage
125 g (4 oz) snow peas
2 white onions, peeled

3 carrots
1 cup (2 oz) bean shoots or
  radish sprouts
500 g (1 lb) raw prawns
  (shrimps), shelled

Dressing

⅓ cup (2⅔ fl oz) lime or
  lemon juice
1½ tablespoons peanut oil
2 teaspoons Oriental
  sesame oil
1 garlic clove, very finely
  chopped

1 tablespoon soy sauce
2 teaspoons sweet chili
  sauce
1 teaspoon sugar

Remove the skin from the fish. Thinly slice the fish. Place in a glass, ceramic or stainless steel bowl and add the lemon juice, peanut and sesame oils and the slivered ginger. Mix lightly but thoroughly. Cover and chill for at least 8 hours.

To prepare the salad, cut the capsicum into julienne. Shred the cabbage, and trim the snow peas. Cut the onions into thin slices from tip to root. Prepare the carrots by shredding or cutting into very fine julienne. Rinse the shoots; pat dry.

Remove the black thread (sand vein) from each prawn and discard. Cut the prawns into pieces. Drain the marinade from the fish strips.

Place the vegetables, fish strips and prawns into a shallow bowl.

To make the dressing, combine all of the ingredients in a jar; shake vigorously until well blended. Pour the dressing over the salad, mix lightly but thoroughly.

Serves 6

NOTE: Vegetables should be well chilled before making the salad.

Grilled · Marinated · Fish · Cutlets

As well as adding delicious depth of flavour, the marinade in this dish tenderises the fish and keeps it beautifully succulent. Sesame oil adds a tantalising nuttiness to the marinade.

Marinade

3 tablespoons chopped green ginger
½ garlic clove, slivered
6 spring onions (scallions), chopped
4 large fish cutlets, such as cod or trevally (about 250 g (8 oz) each)
1 tablespoon lightly toasted sesame seeds
3 tablespoons soy sauce
2 tablespoons dry sherry or rice wine
1½ tablespoons Oriental sesame oil
1 tablespoon finely chopped fresh coriander (cilantro)

Combine all of marinade ingredients in the bowl of a food processor or blender. Mix until smooth. Spread evenly over the fish cutlets. Cover the dish and marinate overnight or for at least 8 hours in the refrigerator.

Heat a barbecue or griller (broiler) to high heat. Grill the fish for 6 to 8 minutes on each side, depending on the thickness of the cutlets. Serve at once, sprinkled with the sesame seeds and coriander.

Serves 4

Fish · with · Szechwan · Sauce

I ate a very similar dish when I was in Macau, and adapted the original recipe to use readily available ingredients.

500 g (1 lb) firm-fleshed boneless fish fillets
2 tablespoons arrowroot or cornflour (cornstarch)
½ teaspoon Chinese 5-Spice powder
⅓ teaspoon coarsely ground Szechwan pepper
⅓ cup (2⅔ fl oz) peanut oil

Szechwan Sauce

2 small red chilies, seeded and finely chopped
4 spring onions (scallions), cut into 2.5 cm (1 inch) lengths
3 garlic cloves, finely chopped
15 g (½ oz) green ginger, finely chopped
½ cup (4 fl oz) cold water
1 tablespoon dry sherry
1 tablespoon soy sauce
1 tablespoon sugar
1 teaspoon rice vinegar or cider vinegar
1 teaspoon Oriental sesame oil
1 teaspoon arrowroot or cornflour (cornstarch)
⅓ teaspoon Szechwan pepper

Remove the skin from the fish fillets; cut the fish into 2.5 cm (1 inch) strips crosswise. Pat dry.

In a bowl, mix together the arrowroot, 5-spice powder and Szechwan pepper. Add the fish slices and toss until lightly but thoroughly covered.

Meantime, heat the peanut oil in a frying pan. Cook the fish in two or three batches until it is crisp and golden brown, about 5 minutes. Remove from the pan with tongs or Chinese wire spoon and drain well on paper towels.

To make the sauce, drain all but 1 tablespoon of oil from the pan, add the prepared chilies, onions, garlic, and green ginger and stir-fry for about 2 minutes.

In a bowl, mix together the water, sherry, soy sauce, sugar, rice vinegar, sesame oil, arrowroot and pepper; stir well. Add to the pan, stirring until the sauce thickens and is clear.

Return the fish to the pan and reheat for only 1 or 2 minutes. Serve immediately.

Serves 4

Stir-fried · Beef with · Julienned · Vegetables

The distinctive flavour of sesame oil gives this dish a character of its own.

500 g (1 lb) rump steak, thinly sliced diagonally
4 small carrots, cut into julienne
250 g (8 oz) snow peas, topped and tailed
250 g (8 oz) oyster mushrooms, sliced
6 spring onions (scallions), cut into 5 cm (1 inch) lengths
1 celery stalk, cut into julienne
3 tablespoons peanut oil
3 tablespoons Oriental sesame oil
¼ cup (2 fl oz) soy sauce
¼ cup (2 fl oz) dry sherry
3 tablespoons toasted sesame seeds

Combine the oils in a wok or heavy pan and set over a moderate heat. Add the steak and carrots and cook for 2 to 3 minutes. Add the snow peas, mushrooms, spring onions and celery and stir fry for 1 to 2 minutes. Stir in the soy sauce and the sherry. Bring to a boil and cook for 1 minute. Sprinkle with the sesame seeds and serve at once with cooked cellophane noodles.

Serves 4

Pork · with · Water · Chestnuts

A very simple version of a popular dish, sesame oil adds interest to the flavour combination it offers. Although water chestnuts do not have a great deal of flavour, they retain their wonderfully crunchy texture during canning and even during cooking and add interest to a recipe such as this.

250 g (3 oz) lean pork, finely diced
1 to 2 tablespoons peanut oil
90 g (3 oz) water chestnuts, sliced
90 g (3 oz) mushrooms, thickly sliced
1 celery stalk, diagonally sliced into thin pieces
1 medium onion, finely sliced

SESAME OIL

1 cup (2 oz) bean shoots
⅓ cup (2⅔ fl oz) cold
   water
1 tablespoon soy sauce
1 tablespoon sherry
1½ teaspoons arrowroot or
   cornflour (cornstarch)

Salt and pepper
1 teaspoon Oriental
   sesame oil
1 tablespoon toasted
   sesame seeds

In a wok, sauté the pork in the heated peanut oil. Add the water chestnuts, mushrooms, celery and onion. Stir-fry for about 3 minutes. Add the bean shoots.

Combine the water, soy sauce, sherry, arrowroot and salt and pepper. Pour into the wok and increase the heat slightly. Bring to a boil, stirring very gently. Simmer for 1 minute, or until the sauce thickens and clears. Remove from the heat, stir in the sesame oil.

Spoon onto a platter and sprinkle with the toasted sesame seeds. Serve immediately, accompanied with crisp-fried noodles cooked in peanut oil.

Serves 3 to 4

Stir-fried · Mushrooms and · Bean · Sprouts

If you have access to exotic mushrooms — either from field or fruiterer — add these to the ingredients. You might like to include a few dried Chinese mushrooms, but do ensure they are well soaked to prevent toughness and chewiness.

Sauce

2 tablespoons oyster sauce
2 tablespoons dry sherry
1 tablespoon light soy
   sauce
2 teaspoons cornflour
   (cornstarch)
1 teaspoon sugar
Freshly ground pepper
½ cup (4 fl oz) cold water

250 g (8 oz) mushrooms
   (abalone oysters, field
   mushrooms, shiitake,
   etc.)
1 garlic clove
About 1 teaspoon coarsely
   chopped green ginger
½ cup (½ oz) fresh
   coriander (cilanto) leaves

OILS

1 cup (8 fl oz) vegetable
oil (or light peanut oil)
2 tablespoons cornflour
(cornstarch)
2 cups (2 handfuls) fresh
bean sprouts
6 spring onions (scallions),
halved lengthwise and cut
into 2.5 cm (1 inch)
lengths
2 tablespoons Oriental
sesame oil
2 tablespoons toasted
sesame seeds

Combine all of the sauce ingredients in a bowl, set aside.

Cut the mushrooms into strips. With the motor running, drop garlic, ginger and coriander into the bowl of a food processor; process until very finely chopped.

Heat the vegetable oil in a wok or deep pan — it needs to be at about 190° C (375° F). Toss half the mushroom strips into the cornflour and fry until they are crisp and browned around the edges; this will take only a few minutes. Drain well on paper towels. Repeat with the remaining mushrooms, ensuring the oil is properly reheated. (The mushrooms will be soggy otherwise.)

Pour off most of the oil; add the bean sprouts and spring onions and cook for about 30 seconds, or until wilted slightly.

Stir the sauce mixture, add to the wok or pan and cook over moderate heat until the sauce simmers and thickens, stirring all the time. Add the mushrooms and immediately spoon the mixture into a shallow serving bowl.

Make a well in the centre and add the garlic/ginger/coriander mixture. Heat the sesame oil in the wok or pan over high heat until it smokes — 35 to 45 seconds — and pour it over the coriander mixture and stir through.

Sprinkle the dish with toasted sesame seeds, and serve at once with steamed rice.

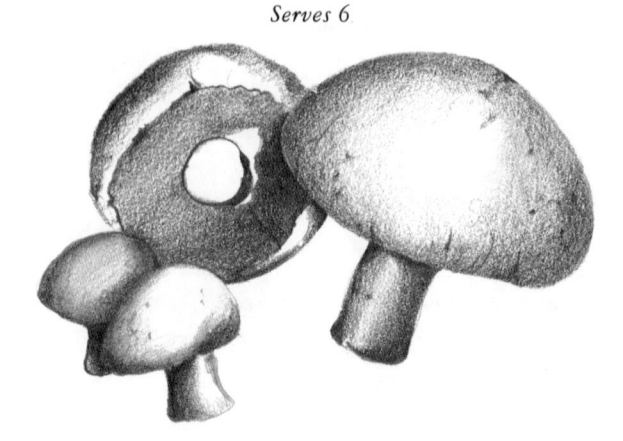

Serves 6

Peanut Oil

The peanut (also known as ground-nut and Arachis nut) is actually a pulse not a nut. When cold pressed, peanut oil is full of peanut flavour, but most peanut oil is refined and almost tasteless.

A mainly monounsaturated oil, it has a smoking point of 210°C (410°F) and so it is suitable for deep-frying. It is also used frequently in Chinese cooking for stir-frying. Because it emulsifies easily, it is excellent for salad dressings, particularly mayonnaise, when the flavour of olive oil might be too powerful. Peanut oil is a versatile oil that should always be on hand.

Devilled · Cashews

Serve these tasty nibbles with drinks or as a snack.

> 3 tablespoons (1½ fl oz) peanut oil
> 250 g (8 oz) roasted cashew nuts
> ½ teaspoon cayenne pepper
> Salt (optional)

Heat the oil in a frying pan. Add the nuts and sauté until heated through. Drain off oil. Sprinkle the nuts with the pepper and salt and quickly stir for a minute. Drain on kitchen paper. Serve warm or cold.

OILS

Chili · Prawns (Shrimps)

Keep a jar of tingly-hot chili oil (see recipe, *page 80*) on your shelves for dishes such as this.

1 cup (8 fl oz) chili oil (see recipe, page 80)	4 garlic cloves, slivered
Juice of 3 lemons	1 kg (about 2¼ lb) prawns (about 36)

Make the marinade by combining the chili oil, lemon juice and garlic in a bowl. To prepare the prawns (shrimps), remove heads but leave the tail intact. Remove dark thread (sand vein). Place the prawns in the marinade, toss lightly. Cover the container and chill overnight.

To cook, preheat the griller (broiler). Remove the prawns from the marinade and arrange in a single layer on a griller pan. Grill (broil) close to the heat until they begin to look opaque, about 2 minutes. Turn and grill for about another 1½ minutes on the other side. Serve immediately.

Serves 6

Pickled · Prawns (Shrimps)

Serve these for guests to munch before a barbecue, or as an interesting addition to a buffet spread.

½ cup (4 fl oz) peanut oil	Few drops of Tabasco sauce
¼ cup (2 fl oz) white wine vinegar	500 g (1 lb) cooked, shelled prawns (shrimps)
1 tablespoon tomato paste	2 small red onions, finely sliced
1 tablespoon Worcestershire sauce	2 bay leaves, torn into pieces
1½ teaspoons brown sugar	
½ teaspoon dry mustard	

In a bowl, blend together the oil, vinegar, tomato paste, Worcestershire sauce, sugar, mustard and Tabasco sauce; mix thoroughly.

Layer the prawns, onions and bay leaves in a shallow dish. Pour on the marinade. Chill for at least 1 hour before serving; this allows the flavours to penetrate the prawns. Serve with the marinade and plenty of thinly-sliced and buttered bread triangles.

Serves 4 to 6

Rabbit · with · Mustard · Sauce

After having become an unfashionable menu item for years, rabbit — a very low cholesterol meat — is making a reappearance on family tables. This is a very tasty dish, excellent for a winter dinner.

> 1 large rabbit, cut into portions, or
> 1 kg (2 lb) prepared rabbit portions
> Dijon mustard
> 2 tablespoons peanut oil
>
> 1 tablespoon chopped mixed herbs
> 1 cup (8 fl oz) dry white wine
> Freshly chopped parsley for garnish

Wash the rabbit pieces and pat dry. Coat the meat with mustard on all sides; arrange in a single layer on a tray and allow to stand for at least 30 minutes.

Heat the oil in a heavy saucepan. Add the rabbit pieces and sauté until well browned on all sides. Be careful it does not stick to the pan! Turn often to prevent burning. Remove the rabbit from the saucepan; set aside and keep warm.

Add the herbs and cook for about 30 seconds. (Add a little more oil, if necessary.) Stir in the wine and keep stirring until heated through. Return the rabbit pieces to the pan and cook, turning the meat often, for about 30 minutes, until tender. Spoon onto a serving platter; pour on the pan sauce. Sprinkle with freshly chopped parsley. Serve with noodles, pasta or rice.

Serves 4

Chicken · Satay · with · Sesame · Seeds

The delightfully distinctive flavour of sesame seeds is heightened by the addition of a little sesame oil. Though this dish should be cooked only at the last minute, most of the preparation can be carried out in advance. For convenience, use a commercially prepared satay sauce. Of course, if preferred, use your own favourite recipe.

OILS

6 chicken breast fillets	1 generous tablespoon
2 tablespoons peanut oil	crunchy peanut butter
2 tablespoons prepared satay sauce	1 teaspoon honey
	1 teaspoon Oriental sesame oil
½ cup (4 fl oz) dry white wine	1½ tablespoons toasted sesame seeds
½ cup (4 fl oz) coconut milk	
¼ cup (2 fl oz) freshly squeezed lemon juice	

Remove the skin from the chicken and discard. Cut the breasts lengthwise into strips. Pour the peanut oil into a wok or deep-frying pan and heat gently. Raise heat to moderately high and stir-fry the chicken strips, turning often. Do not allow them to brown too much; the chicken should be delicately cooked and succulent.

Mix together the satay sauce, wine, coconut milk, lemon juice, peanut butter, honey and sesame oil. Pour into the wok or pan and stir gently. Simmer for about 5 minutes. If it is too thick, add a little water to achieve the desired consistency.

Spoon the chicken and sauce onto serving plates, sprinkle with the toasted sesame seeds. Serve with steamed rice or rice noodles, snow peas, julienned red capsicum (bell pepper) and a lettuce salad.

Serves 6

Snow · Peas · with · Water · Chestnuts and · Mushrooms

This is an excellent vegetable dish to serve with Asian foods or as a light lunch. Baby beans, broccoli florets or asparagus tips may be substituted for the snow peas.

2 to 3 tablespoons peanut oil	4 spring onions (scallions), cut into 2.5 cm (1 inch) lengths (including greens)
250 g (8 oz) can of water chestnuts, drained and sliced	
	500 g (1 lb) fresh snow peas
2 cups (16 oz) champignons, sliced	

PEANUT OIL

½ garlic clove, finely
  chopped
1 tablespoon soy sauce or
  oyster sauce

1 tablespoon cold water

In a wok or large pan with a well-fitting lid, heat the oil. Add the water chestnuts and the champignon slices; cover and cook gently for about 5 minutes.

Add the spring onions, snow peas, garlic, soy sauce and water. Mix well. Cover tightly and simmer for 5 minutes, or until the snow peas are just cooked to tender crispness. Serve immediately.

Serves 6

Salad · of · Summer · Vegetables with · Basil · and · Citrus · Vinaigrette

Great for a summer party, this salad owes a great deal to the delectable flavours of its dressing. The vinaigrette combines olive and peanut oils for economy and flavour and is sparked with the summer fragrance of basil.

12 asparagus spears
1½ cups (4 oz) broccoli
  florets
10 baby carrots

180 g (6 oz) snap peas,
  topped and tailed
10 small yellow "pear"
  tomatoes

Vinaigrette

¾ cup (1½ oz) firmly
  packed basil leaves
1 small white onion,
  chopped
2 tablespoons white wine
  or cider vinegar
Juice of 2 lemons

½ teaspoon sugar
½ teaspoon hot mustard
¾ cup (6 fl oz) peanut oil
¾ cup (6 fl oz) light olive
  oil
Black pepper
Salt (optional)

Prepare the vegetables: blanch separately asparagus spears, broccoli, carrots and snap peas very briefly, refresh under cold running water. Drain well and set aside. Wash the tomatoes.

OILS

To make the vinaigrette, combine the basil leaves, onion, vinegar, lemon juice, sugar and mustard in a food processor or blender. With the motor running, add the combined oils in a thin, steady trickle; process until mixture begins to emulsify. Add pepper and salt to taste.

Arrange the blanched vegetables and tomatoes attractively on a serving platter. Drizzle on the dressing, garnish with fresh basil leaves and lemon slices and serve at once.

Serves 8 to 10

PEANUT OIL

Balinese · Rice · with · Peanut · Sauce

The ingredients for this tasty vegetarian dish may be prepared in advance and cooked just when required. The sauce will keep for several days under refrigeration.

3 cups (12 oz) cold cooked brown rice
250 g (8 oz) green beans
½ small cabbage
4 small carrots
4 hard-boiled eggs, sliced
1 teaspoon Oriental sesame oil

Peanut Sauce

1 onion, finely chopped
1 very small finely chopped red chili pepper
1 cup (8 fl oz) water
½ cup (4 oz) crunchy peanut butter
1 teaspoon sugar
1 teaspoon cider vinegar
1 tablespoon of peanut oil
Black pepper
1 tablespoon finely chopped coriander (cilantro) or parsley

Remove strings and cut beans into 2.5 cm (1 inch) lengths; cut carrots into julienne; finely shred the cabbage.

One at a time, cook vegetables lightly in boiling water; drain well and let cool. When quite cold, mix through the rice with the sesame oil.

To make the sauce, sauté the onion in the heated oil. Add chili, water, peanut butter and sugar. Bring slowly to the boil, stirring constantly until mixture is smooth. Stir in the vinegar. Season with black pepper and coriander. Cool to room temperature.

Pour the sauce over the vegetables, arrange sliced hard-boiled eggs on top and serve.

Serves 4 to 6

OILS

Chili · Oil

Use this oil to add interest to rice dishes, salads, dressings, Mexican food or to brown meats for stews and casseroles.

6 small red chilies, quartered and seeded   *2 cups (16 fl oz) peanut oil*

Combine the chilies and oil in a large jar; cover tightly. Allow to stand for at least 2 weeks before testing for flavour. Taste after this time and if the oil is hot enough, strain off the chilies and bottle the oil. If a stronger flavour is preferred, leave the chilies in the oil for another week. A few chili seeds included in the oil will add extra "heat"!

Makes 2 cups (16 fl oz)

NOTE: It is important to wear rubber gloves or to thoroughly wash your hands after handling these fierce little chilies. Do not put your fingers near your eyes after touching them.

Soy Oil

Soy oil is often the main component of oils described simply as vegetable oil. An unsaturated oil, it has a smoking point of 210°C (410°F). Although it is bland in flavour and pale in colour it has a strong smell when heated. It won't contribute much to a salad dressing, but it is an economical choice for deep or shallow frying. It also has widespread industrial use in paints, plastics, insecticides etc.

Spicy · Pork · Satays

It is the tangy marinade that gives this pork satay its exciting flavour. It is important to allow the marinade to "work" for at least 8 hours — longer, if possible.

Marinade

½ cup (4 fl oz) honey, warmed
4 garlic cloves, crushed or finely chopped
2 teaspoons chopped fresh ginger
1 teaspoon chili powder
1 cup (8 oz) unsweetened pineapple juice
1 cup (8 oz) soy oil
2 tablespoons (1 fl oz) light soy sauce
1 tablespoon chopped fresh sage or 1½ teaspoons dried sage
1½ kg (3¼ lb) lean pork, cubed

Combine the warm honey with the garlic and ginger; stir in the chili powder. Mix together the pineapple juice, oil, soy sauce and sage and stir into the honey mixture.

Place the pork into the marinade, stir to ensure it is well covered. Allow to marinate for 12 hours.

Thread the meat onto satay sticks which have been well soaked in water (this prevents them charring). Cook under the griller (broiler) or on the barbecue. Serve with Peanut Sauce (*below*).

Peanut Sauce

1 tablespoon peanut oil
1 small white onion, finely chopped
3 garlic cloves, finely chopped
1 teaspoon chili powder
1 teaspoon finely chopped green ginger
1 cup (8 oz) crunchy peanut butter
2 tablespoons vinegar or lemon juice
1 tablespoon light soy sauce
1 cup (8 fl oz) coconut milk

Heat oil, sauté onion, garlic, chili and ginger until just softened. Add all remaining ingredients except for coconut milk. Raise heat slightly and gradually stir in coconut milk; do not boil.

Serves 10

Safflower Oil

This mainly polyunsaturated oil is often used in special diet mayonnaise and other salad dressings. The safflower originated in India, where it was grown for its oil (to burn in lamps), and for the dye from its petals. Its lack of flavour makes it a versatile oil for shallow frying or cake-making, but an unexciting choice for salad dressings.

Omelette · of · Spring · Herbs

2 eggs
1 tablespoon cold water
Freshly ground pepper
2 tablespoons safflower oil

1½ tablespoons finely
chopped fresh herbs such
as French tarragon,
chives, chervil, parsley,
basil, etc.

Lightly mix together the eggs, cold water and pepper. Heat the oil in a small pan, tilting the pan until the surface is coated with the oil.

Pour in the egg mixture, shaking the pan constantly. Cook gently until lightly browned underneath and surface is beginning to lightly firm. Sprinkle on the chopped herbs, cook for another minute. Fold omelette in half and serve at once. Add a fresh green salad for a delicious contrast of textures.

Serves 1

Herbed · Spinach

An appetising dish to serve a vegetarian — healthy and with appealing flavour.

About 500 g (1 lb) spinach
or silver beet
2 tablespoons safflower oil
1 white onion, chopped
1 garlic clove finely
chopped
1 teaspoon chopped fresh
parsley

Freshly ground pepper
½ teaspoon chopped fresh
rosemary (optional)
½ cup (2 oz) grated tasty
(sharp or Jack) cheese

Wash the spinach and shake off the moisture. Cut the leaves into thick shreds.

Heat the oil in a heavy saucepan. Add the onion and sauté until translucent. Add the spinach, garlic, parsley, pepper and rosemary. Cook over very low heat, stirring often.

To serve, sprinkle with the grated cheese and additional pepper.

Serves 4

Curried · Cauliflower

Another excellent recipe for a vegetarian who appreciates good food. Serve it as part of a curry feast.

1 medium cauliflower
3 tablespoons safflower oil
2 onions, finely chopped
2 tablespoons chopped fresh mint, or 2 tablespoons chopped fresh coriander (cilantro)
1 teaspoon turmeric
1 teaspoon ground cumin
1 teaspoon dry mustard
½ teaspoon ground cinnamon
½ teaspoon ground ginger
Black pepper
½ cup (4 fl oz) water
500 g (1 lb) ripe tomatoes, chopped

Cut the cauliflower into florets; wash and dry. Heat the oil; sauté the onion. Blend together the mint, spices, pepper and water; stir until the consistency of a paste. Add to the onion and cook for 5 minutes. Add the tomatoes and cook for another 5 minutes. Add the cauliflower pieces and cook only until crisp-tender.

Serves 4 to 6

NOTE: If preferred, cauliflower florets may be partly cooked first by dropping the pieces into boiling water and simmering for 5 to 6 minutes then draining before cooking as suggested above.

Mayonnaise

This recipe makes an alternative mayonnaise for those who prefer to use a polyunsaturated oil as the basis. The flavour is less distinctive than when olive oil is used but still provides a very good dressing. Make it in a blender or food processor for convenience.

1 whole egg
2 egg yolks
1 tablespoon mild prepared mustard
3 tablespoons lemon juice or white wine vinegar

2 cups (16 fl oz) safflower oil
Salt (optional)
Freshly ground pepper

Combine the egg, egg yolks, mustard and lemon juice in the bowl of a food processor or blender. Blend for about 30 seconds.

With the motor running, pour in the oil in a very thin, slow and steady stream. When the mixture begins to thicken, turn off the machine. Using a spatula, scrape sides of the bowl. Taste and adjust seasoning, if necessary.

Spoon the mayonnaise into a covered container and store in the refrigerator until required. It will last for about 5 days. Always use it at room temperature.

Makes about 2½ cups (20 fl oz)

NOTE: If planning to store the mayonnaise for several days, stir in 1 tablespoon of boiling water before chilling. This prevents it from thickening.

Soybean · Health · Loaf

Ideal for vegetarians, this may be served hot or cold, with vegetables or salads.

2½ cups (5 oz) cooked soybeans
1 cup (4 oz) cooked brown rice, well drained
¼ cup (3 oz) crunchy peanut butter

2 tablespoons wheat germ
1 large tomato, finely chopped
1 cup finely grated carrot
1 celery stalk, finely chopped

SAFFLOWER OIL

> 1 small white onion, finely
>   chopped
> 3 tablespoons safflower oil
> 1 teaspoon chopped
>   French tarragon
> Sea salt (optional)
> ½ teaspoon ground cumin

Mash the soybeans or puree them in a food processor. Combine all ingredients in a large bowl, mixing thoroughly until well blended.

Spoon into a greased loaf tin or casserole. Bake at 175°C (350°F), uncovered, for 45 minutes. Allow to stand for a few minutes before cutting; this prevents crumbling.

Serves 4 to 5

NOTE: If desired, grated cheese may be sprinkled on top before baking the loaf.

Banana · and · Carrot · Cake

Over the last few years cakes using oil as the shortening ingredient have become very popular. An ideal family cake, they are nutritious (compared with some wicked cakes!), easy to make and long-lasting. It is worthwhile making a double quantity and freezing one cake for a later occasion.

> 2 eggs
> ¾ cup (3 oz) raw sugar
> Grated zest of 1 lemon
> ¾ cup (6 fl oz) safflower
>   oil
> 1½ cups (6 oz) self-raising
>   flour
> 1 ripe banana, mashed
> 1 cup (4 oz) grated carrot
> ¾ cup (3 oz) crushed
>   pineapple, well drained
> ½ cup (2 oz) chopped
>   walnuts

Beat together the eggs and sugar; stir in the lemon zest. Gradually add the oil, beating constantly. Sift the flour. Add to the egg mixture. Stir in the banana, carrot, crushed pineapple and walnuts.

Pour the mixture into a well-greased 20 cm (8 inch) cake tin. Bake in a preheated 180°C (375°F) oven for 50 to 60 minutes. Cool on a wire rack.

Crumble-crusted · Date · Squares

These are splendid for lunchboxes or after-school snacks, especially for those with an intolerance for dairy products.

1½ cups (7 oz) chopped dates
1¼ cups (10 fl oz) water
Juice of ½ lemon
2 teaspoons grated orange zest

Crumble Crust

2 cups (10 oz) rolled oats
1 cup (4 oz) wholemeal (whole wheat) flour
Grated zest of ½ lemon
¼ cup (2 fl oz) safflower oil
¼ cup (2 fl oz) honey, warmed

To making the filling, simmer the dates in the water until soft. Mash with the lemon juice and the orange zest.

Mix the dry ingredients for the topping in a bowl. Stir in the oil and warmed honey and mix in with fingertips until the mixture is the consistency of coarse breadcrumbs. Pat about ⅔ of it into an oiled 20 cm (8 inch) baking tin, spread evenly. Add the fruit filling and spread right to the edges of the crumble base. Sprinkle the remaining crumb mixture on top, press lightly.

Bake in a preheated 170°C (350°F) oven for about 45 minutes. Allow to cool before cutting into squares.

Makes 16 small squares

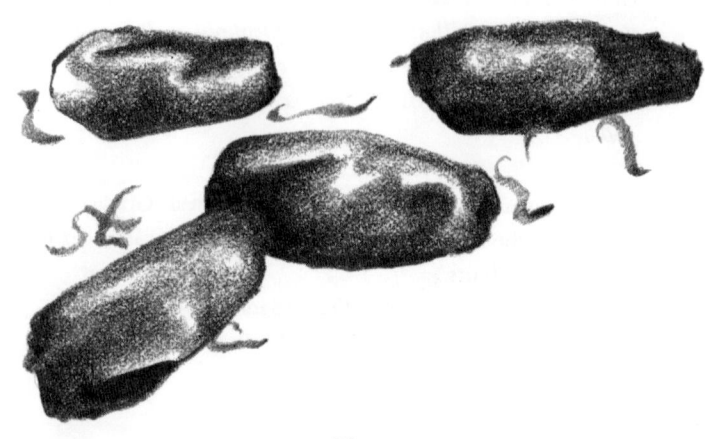

SAFFLOWER OIL

Apple · and · Maple · Syrup · Muffins

Muffins provide a delicious breakfast treat or daytime snack. Make up a double batch and freeze half — *if* you can resist the temptation to eat the whole lot!

> 1 cup (4 oz) plain (all-purpose) flour
> 1 cup (4 oz) wholemeal (whole wheat) flour
> 1 cup (8 fl oz) milk
> 1/3 cup (2 2/3 fl oz) maple syrup
>
> 1/4 cup (2 fl oz) safflower oil
> 1 large egg
> 1 cup peeled, grated cooking apple

Combine the flours in a mixing bowl. In another bowl, combine the milk, maple syrup, oil, egg and grated apple. Add the dry ingredients and stir lightly with a wooden spoon until just blended. It is important not to overmix muffins; the texture should still be lumpy.

Spoon the mixture into 12 buttered muffin tins. Bake at 180°C (350°F) for 20 to 25 minutes, or until muffins are risen and golden brown. Serve warm, lightly buttered.

Makes 12

Blackberry · Muffins

Make these delectable muffins on a day in late summer when you have found a patch of sun-warmed blackberries. More and more difficult to find now as we become nations of city dwellers, it is still worth seeking out a "prickle patch".

> 185 g (6 oz) ripe blackberries
> 125 g (4 oz) plus 1 tablespoon castor (granulated) sugar
> 185 g (6 oz) plain (all-purpose) flour
> 1 1/4 teaspoons baking powder
>
> 6 tablespoons (3 fl oz) milk
> 6 tablespoons (3 fl oz) safflower oil
> 1 large egg, beaten
> Icing (confectioners') sugar or castor (granulated) sugar
> Ground cinnamon

OILS

Remove the stems from the blackberries; wipe berries clean. Mix them with 1 tablespoon of castor sugar.

Sift together the flour and baking powder. Lightly mix in the milk, the remaining 125 g (4 oz) sugar, oil and egg. Gently stir in the blackberries, being careful not to crush them. It is important that muffins should never be over-mixed, so stir only until the ingredients are lightly mixed together.

Spoon the mixture into 18 well buttered muffin tins, filling each about ⅔ full. Bake in a preheated moderate oven 180°C (350°F) for 20 minutes, or until risen and golden.

Remove the muffins from the tins. Sprinkle each muffin with a mixture of icing or castor sugar and ground cinnamon. Serve warm with butter.

Makes 18

NOTE: As these muffins freeze well, it is worthwhile making up a double quantity and storing away a "squirrel stock" in your freezer.

Happiness · Cookies

The "alternative lifestyler" who gave me this recipe back in the '70s assured me they were a favourite snack on the commune where she lived. The original recipe called for soy flour, but I have used wholemeal flour with satisfactory results.

1 cup (4 oz) soy or wholemeal flour
1 teaspoon baking powder
1 cup (2 oz) wheat germ
1 egg
½ cup (4 fl oz) honey
½ cup (4 fl oz) milk
¼ cup (2 fl oz) safflower oil
¼ cup (1 oz) chopped almonds
¼ cup (1 oz) chopped dates
¼ cup (1 oz) raisins

Stir together the flour and baking powder. Stir in the wheat germ.

Mix together the egg, honey, milk and oil; stir into the flours. Add the nuts, dates and raisins; mix well.

Form tablespoonfuls of the mixture into balls; place on greased oven trays. Flatten each with a knife dipped into milk.

Bake in a preheated 180°C (375°F) oven for about 20 minutes. Loosen with a knife when cooked; cool on trays.

Makes 24

NOTE: For a change, substitute or add some chopped apricots to the dried fruits.

Sunflower Oil

Sunflower oil is one of the most popular oils for household use and widely used in the manufacture of margarine. It is unsaturated and has a smoking point of 200°C (392°F), making it suitable for deep or shallow frying. It is also used in salad dressings and cake-making.

Herb · Cheese · Spread

This zesty spread is great served with crackers or with crispy vegetable crudités. Well sealed, it will keep in the refrigerator for up to 3 weeks. This makes it a useful item to have on hand when guests drop in unexpectedly!

90 g (3 oz) cream cheese, at room temperature
1½ tablespoons finely chopped mixed herbs (such as basil, rosemary, thyme, parsley, marjoram, chives)
1 teaspoon dry mustard
⅓ cup (2⅔ fl oz) sherry wine
¼ cup (2 fl oz) sunflower seed oil
500 g (1 lb) finely grated Cheddar cheese (tasty, medium tasty or mild)
Freshly ground pepper

SUNFLOWER OIL

Combine the cream cheese, herbs and mustard. Add the sherry and oil and blend well. (An electric hand beater works very well.) Fold in the grated cheese and the pepper. Spoon the mixture into a bowl; cover and chill for several hours.

Makes about 3 cups (24 oz)

NOTE: This spread makes a nice gift if it is packed into small, attractive crocks, accompanied by a small paté knife, a package of crackers and the recipe for this spread.

Cashew · Nut · Butter

This excellent butter is a pleasant change from peanut butter; you can blend it to a smooth or crunchy texture, to suit your own preferences. A bland oil is the best choice for allowing the full flavours of the cashews to develop.

250 g (8 oz) roasted cashew nuts	3 tablespoons sunflower or safflower oil

Combine the nuts and oil in the bowl of a food processor or blender; using an off/on motion, process the butter until the desired texture is achieved.

If it is to be kept for any time, cover tightly and chill. However, it is easier to spread at room temperature.

Tempura

This popular Japanese dish depends for its success on the lightness and crispness of the delicate batter. It is important to cook it at the very last minute and, unlike most batter recipes, this one should be made only when the meal is to be cooked. Sunflower oil, light and bland in flavour, is a good choice for this recipe.

Make sure vegetables and prawns are as dry as possible — this helps ensure crispness.

OILS

250 g (8 oz) button
   mushrooms
185 g (6 oz) broccoli
   florets
185 g (6 oz) asparagus tips

About 24 large green
   (uncooked) prawns
   (shrimps), shelled but
   with tails intact

Sauce for Dipping

3 tablespoons Japanese soy
   sauce (such as
   Kikkoman)
3 tablespoons dry sherry

3 tablespoons rich chicken
   stock
1 teaspoon finely shredded
   ginger

Tempura Batter

1 medium egg
½ cup (4 fl oz) cold water
90 g (3 oz) plain (all-
   purpose) flour

30 g (1 oz) cornflour
   (cornstarch)
Sunflower oil for deep
   frying

Prepare the vegetables and prawns and arrange on platters.

Combine the ingredients for the dipping sauce and pour into individual tiny bowls or one larger one.

To make the batter, beat the egg and water together. Sift the flours into another bowl. Pour in sufficient oil to reach about ⅓ of the way up a deep saucepan or use a deep fryer. Heat the oil to 180°C (350°F). Whisk the flours into the combined egg/water mixture, whisking until quite smooth.

Dip each piece of vegetable or prawn into the batter and put carefully into the hot oil. Do not crowd the pan; it is essential that the oil should maintain its hot temperature. Drain each piece as it is cooked — this should take no more than a couple of minutes — using a slotted spoon or tongs. Serve immediately; pass the dipping sauce separately.

Serves 4

Mexican · Rice

2 medium onions, finely chopped
2 garlic cloves, finely chopped
3 tablespoons sunflower oil
1 cup (5 oz) long-grain rice
2 cups (6 fl oz) canned tomatoes, drained and coarsely chopped
4 tablespoons chopped canned mild green chili peppers
2 cups (16 fl oz) chicken stock
Freshly ground pepper

Sauté the onions and garlic in the heated oil. Add the rice and cook until the onions are tender and the rice is lightly coloured. Stir in the tomatoes, chili peppers and stock. Bring to a boil.

Reduce the heat and simmer, covered, until the rice is tender and all of the liquid is absorbed, about 30 minutes.

Add pepper to taste.

Serves 6

Tarragon · Lamb · Cutlets

Traditionally lamb is accompanied by mint, but this dish offers a change of herb which is delightful. Choose baby lamb cutlets, trim them well, and you have a gourmet delight.

8 lamb cutlets (well trimmed)
Salt (optional)
Freshly ground pepper

Marinade

3 tablespoons sunflower oil
2 garlic cloves, crushed
¼ cup (2 fl oz) dry white wine
1 teaspoon coarse-grained mustard

OILS

> 2 tablespoons tarragon
>   vinegar
> 2 tablespoons tomato paste
> 1 tablespoon finely
>   chopped French
>   tarragon
>
> Few sprigs French
>   tarragon, for garnish

Lightly flatten the cutlets with a cleaver or wooden mallet (or even with a bottle). Sprinkle them with a little salt and pepper; set aside.

Make the marinade by combining all of the ingredients and mixing well. Place the cutlets in a shallow dish, pour on the marinade. Cover and refrigerate for at least 2 hours, turning the meat once or twice during that time.

Drain the cutlets, reserving the marinade. Place the cutlets under a preheated griller (broiler) and cook lightly, brushing with the marinade once or twice. Turn and cook the other side, again brushing with marinade.

Serve with mashed potatoes, baby peas and a green salad. Garnish plate with fresh tarragon sprigs.

Serves 4

NOTE: If cutlets are very small, it may be necessary to allow three per serving.

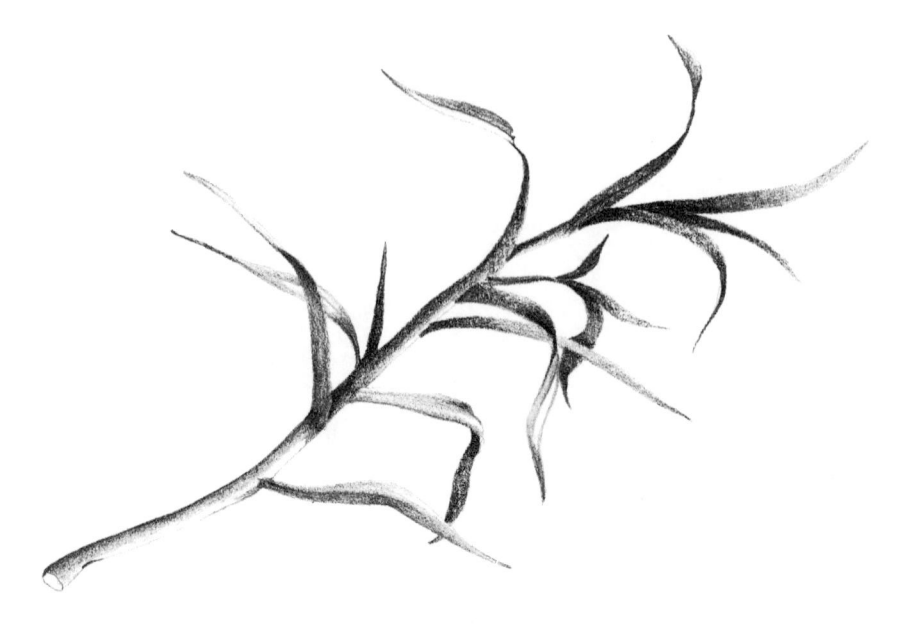

Cinnamon · Pumpkin · Bread

This loaf has a wonderfully warm and sweet flavour; ideal for afternoon teas or for school lunches.

1¾ cups (7 oz) self-raising flour, or
1¾ cups (7 oz) plain (all-purpose) flour sifted with 1 teaspoon baking powder
1 teaspoon ground cinnamon
½ teaspoon ground nutmeg
⅓ teaspoon ground cloves
1 cup (7 oz) castor (granulated) sugar
½ cup (4 fl oz) sunflower oil
2 eggs
1 cup (4 oz) cooked, drained and well mashed pumpkin
¼ cup (2 fl oz) water

Butter and flour a 23 x 13 x 6 cm (9 x 5 x 2½ inch) loaf tin.

Sift together the flour and spices. Combine sugar, oil and eggs in a bowl or food processor. Mix until light and fluffy. Gradually add the pumpkin and dry ingredients alternately with the water, beating only until ingredients are mixed; be careful not to overbeat.

Spoon the mixture into the prepared tin. Place in a preheated 180°C (350°F) oven and bake on the middle shelf for 65 to 70 minutes, or until a wooden satay stick inserted into the loaf comes out clean. Cool in the tin for 5 minutes. Turn out onto a rack to cool completely.

Makes 1 loaf

Golden · Cake

Wonderfully moist and flavoursome, this cake keeps particularly well, which of course makes it ideal for lunches.

¾ cup (4 oz) raw sugar
½ cup (4 fl oz) sunflower oil
2 eggs
1½ cups (6 oz) plain (all-purpose) flour

1 teaspoon baking powder
1 teaspoon bicarbonate of
   soda (baking soda)
1 teaspoon ground
   cinnamon

½ teaspoon mixed spices
3 medium carrots, peeled
   and finely grated
1 cup (6 oz) well-drained
   crushed canned pineapple

Combine sugar, oil and eggs and beat until light and creamy. Sift together flour, baking powder, soda and spices. Add the carrots and the sugar/oil mixture and stir together. Lightly mix in the pineapple, ensuring mixture is well blended.

Spoon the mixture into a large buttered and floured loaf tin. Bake in a preheated 180°C (350°F) oven for 50 to 60 minutes. To test the cake, press lightly with a fingertip; if it springs back, the cake is cooked.

Cool in the tin for about 10 minutes; turn out onto a wire rack and cool completely. When quite cold, frost with Cream Cheese Frosting (*below*).

Cream Cheese Frosting

125 g (4 oz) cream cheese
30 g (1 oz) butter, softened
1 tablespoon lemon juice

1¼ cups (7 oz) sifted icing
   (confectioners') sugar

Combine the cream cheese, butter and lemon juice and beat until smooth. Gradually add the icing sugar and beat until fluffy. Chill slightly. Spread over the top and sides of the cake. Sprinkle with ground cinnamon, toasted coconut or toasted, chopped walnuts or pecans.

Makes 1 loaf

Grapeseed Oil

Most grapeseed oil comes from the French wine growing areas. It was first produced during World War I when other oils were scarce. Bland in flavour and light in texture, its high smoking point 230° C (446° F) makes it ideal for deep-frying.

It has the highest percentage of polyunsaturated fatty acids of any cooking oil.

Buy it in small quantites, because it tends to go rancid quickly.

Tahina

This popular dip or spread appears on most Middle Eastern menus, whether in the restaurant or in a private home. I ate it almost every day on a recent trip, and it varied from house to house and restaurant to restaurant. This is a version I developed, based on the quantities in a recipe I was given in Tel Aviv.

150 g (5 oz) sesame seeds
½ cup (4 fl oz) water
2 garlic cloves, chopped
Juice of 2 lemons
Salt (optional)
Good pinch of cayenne
Grapeseed oil
1 teaspoon Oriental sesame oil

Combine the sesame seeds, water, garlic, lemon juice, salt and cayenne in a blender. Blend to a purée. Gradually add the grapeseed oil until the required consistency is achieved. (I like it to be that of fairly runny peanut butter.) Stir in the sesame oil — this adds a wonderfully rich flavour.

Makes about 1¼ cups (10 fl oz)

Pasta · Salad · with · Smoked · Salmon and · Caviar

Cold pasta has become a popular addition to summer tables over the last year or so, and this is one dish that I have found to be very well received. Because of the delicate flavours of the other ingredients, I like to use gentle grapeseed oil for this recipe.

Dressing

⅓ cup (2⅔ fl oz) grapeseed oil
2 small French shallots (scallions) or 1 small white onion, finely chopped
2 tablespoons lemon juice
¼ cup (1 handful) chopped fresh dill or chervil
Freshly ground black pepper
250 g (8 oz) spiral pasta
1 cup (16 whole) cherry tomatoes, halved

2 tablespoons finely chopped chives
185 g (6 oz) smoked salmon, cut into slivers
60 g (2 oz) red or black caviar
1 small salad onion, thinly sliced
¾ cup (6 fl oz) cultured sour cream
Fresh dill

Make the dressing by combining the grapeseed oil, shallots, lemon juice, dill and pepper; whisk until well blended.

Cook the pasta in a large saucepan filled with lightly salted boiling water. Pour a little oil onto the water to prevent the pasta sticking and drop the pasta into the water in small quantities, so that the water keeps boiling. Drain pasta well, add a dash more oil and lightly stir as it cools to prevent the pasta spirals clinging together.

When the pasta is almost cold, add the dressing, tomatoes, chives and half the smoked salmon; mix together very lightly. Set aside for about 30 minutes to allow the flavours to blend.

To serve, spoon the pasta onto a large serving platter; top with remaining smoked salmon strips, caviar and dill sprigs. Spoon the sour cream on top; garnish with dill sprigs.

Serves 4 to 6

Marinated · Champignons

Serve these tasty little mouthfuls with a pre-dinner drink or as a salad on a buffet table. Either tiny fresh champignons or whole canned champignons may be used; the texture and flavour will differ accordingly, but both are very good eating. The delicacy of grapeseed oil suits this dish very well; for a more robust flavour, substitute olive oil.

2 cups (16 oz) canned whole champignons, or 250 g (8 oz) fresh champignons
2 spring onions (scallions), finely chopped
1 tablespoon finely chopped fresh dill or parsley

1 bay leaf, torn
Black pepper
½ cup (4 fl oz) grapeseed oil
1 tablespoon white wine vinegar
½ garlic clove, slivered (optional)

Rinse and drain canned mushrooms; lightly sauté fresh mushrooms for 2 minutes in a little heated olive oil. (Fresh mushrooms will absorb oil very quickly.)

In a bowl, combine mushrooms, onion, dill, bay leaf and pepper. Whisk together the oil and vinegar; add the garlic. Pour over the mushrooms. Mix well. Allow to stand for several hours at least, stirring lightly from time to time.

To serve, drain lightly and sprinkle with a little chopped fresh dill or parsley.

Serves 4 to 6

NOTE: For a change of flavour, substitute different herbs such as basil, thyme, lemon verbena, marjoram, mint, etc.

The marinated champignons will keep well under refrigeration for up to a week.

OILS

Celery · Fennel · Avocado · and · Cherry · Tomato · Salad

This unusual combination of salad ingredients offers wonderful flavours as well as a delightful range of textures. The voluptuous satiny texture of the avocado contrasts beautifully with the crispy crunch of celery and fennel. The delicacy of the grapeseed oil provides the perfect base for the tangy flavours of the citrus juices in the dressing.

1 large Florence fennel bulb
1 small crisp celery stalk
250 g (8 oz) ripe cherry tomatoes
2 medium-size firm but ripe avocadoes

Dressing

Grated zest and juice of 1 large orange
Grated zest and juice of 1 lime or lemon
¼ cup (2 fl oz) grapeseed oil
1 to 2 teaspoons white wine vinegar
1 teaspoon coarse-grained mild mustard
Freshly ground black pepper

Peel off any coarse outer leaves of the fennel; reserve any fronds. Cut the crisp inner flesh of the fennel into strips, from top to base. Cut celery into julienne or thin diagonal slices. Halve the tomatoes. Peel the avocadoes and cut into slices. Arrange all of the salad ingredients on an attractive serving platter.

Whisk together dressing ingredients; taste and adjust seasoning if necessary. Pour a portion of the dressing over the salad. Garnish with the reserved fennel fronds. Pass the remaining dressing separately.

Serves 6 to 8

GRAPESEED OIL

Yoghurt · Salad · Dressing

I like this dressing with cucumber, cold poached fish or even potato salad. Do not make it too far in advance, otherwise the yoghurt tends to become watery.

1 cup (8 fl oz) natural yoghurt	Salt (optional)
1 tablespoon grapeseed oil	Freshly ground pepper
2 teaspoons Dijon mustard	2 tablespoons finely chopped herbs such as
1 teaspoon castor (granulated) sugar	dill, tarragon, mixed fresh herbs, mint, etc.

Mix together all of the ingredients except the herbs, stirring well to blend. Adjust the flavours by adding more sugar, salt or pepper, if necessary. Stir in the herbs.

For a variety of flavours, add a few drops of Tabasco sauce, cumin powder, chili powder, curry powder or coarse-grained mustard.

Makes about 1 cup (8 fl oz)

Avocado · Mayonnaise

This is an excellent mayonnaise to serve with cold chicken, fish or green salad. If it is made too far in advance, it may discolour. Discolouration may be reduced by pouring a little extra oil onto the mayonnaise after it is made; this can be stirred in at serving time.

1 large ripe avocado	3 tablespoons grapeseed oil
1 large egg	1 teaspoon Dijon mustard
Juice of 1 lemon	White pepper

Halve the avocado, discard seed and scoop out the flesh. Chop the flesh and place into the bowl of a blender or food processor. Add the egg to the avocado and lightly mix in; add the lemon juice. Gradually pour in the oil whilst motor is running. Add the mustard and pepper and blend until smooth.

Spoon into a container, pour a thin film of oil onto the surface (if not using immediately) and chill until ready to serve.

Makes about 1 cup (8 fl oz)

Corn (Maize) Oil

Unlike most vegetable oils, corn oil has a strong colour reminiscent of wine and toasted corn. An unsaturated oil, it has a smoking point of 210°C (410°F) and it is good for deep and shallow frying. It is popular in the United States, which produces about 70 percent of the world's corn oil.

Southern · Chicken

The use of corn oil gives the traditional flavour we expect from this dish. It is important to ensure that the oil is HOT — this seals the coating quickly and creates a crisp coating. Delicious served with freshly boiled sweet corn cobs.

>   Corn oil for frying
>   1 cup (4 oz) plain (all-purpose) flour
>   Plenty of pepper
>   2 large whole chicken breasts, halved

In a large pan, heat about 2.5 cm (1 inch) corn oil until surface quivers and the oil reaches about 185°C (375°F). Sift the flour and season with pepper; coat the chicken just before cooking.

Place the chicken pieces carefully into the hot oil and cook for 10 minutes. Turn chicken and cook for another 15 minutes or until crisp and golden. Drain chicken well on paper towels. Serve very hot.

Serves 4

CORN (MAIZE) OIL

A · Relish · of · Chives

This most unusual relish is delicious served with cold meat or chicken. A great way of using up the greens from a rampant clump of chives in the vegetable patch!

½ cup (1 oz) finely chopped chive greens
½ cup (4 fl oz) corn oil
1 tablespoon cider vinegar
Freshly ground pepper
3 hard-boiled eggs, finely mashed or pushed through a sieve

Combine all of the ingredients in a bowl and mix very thoroughly until well blended. Store in refrigerator.

Makes about 1 cup (8 oz)

NOTE: This is excellent used as a spread on a sandwich of tasty cheese.

OILS

Curried · Cottage · Cheese · Dressing

This protein rich dressing is excellent served with hot or cold cooked asparagus, broad beans, broccoli or cauliflower.

250 g (8 oz) cottage cheese
½ cup (4 fl oz) corn oil
1 teaspoon curry powder
1 tablespoon finely chopped parsley
Good squeeze of lemon juice
Freshly ground pepper

Combine all of the ingredients in a processor and purée, or beat until well blended with an electric hand mixer.

Extra · Cornbread

This is excellent served barely warm. Chewy and delicious, serve it with salads or soups.

1 cup (4 oz) cornmeal
1 cup (4 oz) wholemeal (whole wheat) flour
2 teaspoons baking powder
Salt (optional)
1½ cups (12 fl oz) milk
2 tablespoons honey
⅓ cup (2⅔ fl oz) corn oil

Sift the dry ingredients together, returning any coarse particles to the mixing bowl. Stir together the milk and honey, add the oil and mix well.

Make a well in the centre of the dry ingredients, pour in the liquid. Mix only until the dry ingredients are moistened — DO NOT OVERMIX!

Pour the mixture into an oiled 20 cm (8 inch) baking tin.

Bake in a preheated 210°C (425°F) oven for about 25 minutes, or until the cornbread is well risen and golden brown.

Makes 1 loaf

Herb Oils

Herb oils are a delightful addition to the pantry shelf but expensive to buy. It makes sense to make your own — you'll save money and have the fun of creating your own flavour combinations.

Most herbs are suitable for flavouring oils, but some are particularly good. I like to have a selection of individual flavours, such as thyme, bay leaf, rosemary and garlic, and another of mixed herbs. My particular favourite is basil, and I have a large decanter of basil oil always close at hand on my kitchen bench. Often when I need inspiration, its rich translucent green-gold colour catches my eye — and in goes a splash to transform a basic dish into something more interesting.

The choice of oil is up to you. Pure olive oil is fine if the flavoured oil is to be mainly used for cooking, or in mayonnaise. Herb-flavoured extra-virgin olive oil is superb sprinkled on salads or on cooked meat or fish. And you may like to try some other oils as well — for example, cold pressed peanut oil is wonderful with chilis or ginger.

Always wash and dry the herbs first. When using hard-leaved herbs, I like to warm the oil a little, but with tender-leaved herbs, such as basil and dill, I find room-temperature oil works just as well. Pour the oil over the herbs (about one cup (8 fl oz) oil to six sprigs rosemary or eight fresh bay leaves, is a rough guide), and seal the jar or bottle when the oil is cool. Leave it for two or three weeks in a cool, dark place. Taste the oil after two weeks

OILS

HERB OILS

and if the flavour has developed sufficiently, it's ready to use. I don't always remove the herbs (if hard-leaved), although many people like to strain the oil and pour it into a clean bottle containing just one sprig of the herb. If an oil becomes too strong I dilute it with unflavoured oil.

When making rosemary oil, I dry the rosemary for a few days to avoid the cloudiness that fresh rosemary seems to create.

You can also make oil from dried herbs. Be careful with the quantity as dried herbs are more potent than fresh herbs — start with three-quarters of a teaspoon of herbs to one cup (8 fl oz) of oil.

Although not strictly a herbal oil, I also like to steep orange or lemon zest in oil. This citrus oil is particularly delicious when used to brown meats for casseroles, or sprinkled on warm vegetables.

A few peppercorns, a star anise, or other attractive spices will also add flavour and improve the appearance of a herb oil.

Rosemary · Oil

This may be used to sauté meats or vegetables and is also very pleasant to use as a massage oil or to add to a bath. Coarsely chopped fresh pine needles also provide a fragrant body oil — use the same method.

4½ tablespoons rosemary sprigs

600 ml (19 fl oz) light olive oil

Rub the rosemary lightly between hands to release the volatile oils, then place into a wide mouthed jar. Pour in the oil.

Allow to stand for about 3 weeks before straining and rebottling.

Makes 600 ml (19 fl oz)

Index

Aïoli 16
Almond oil 61
Apple and maple syrup muffins 89
Artichokes, suppli with olives and 20
Asparagus
  vegetarian salad delight 39
  vinaigrette 16
Autumn salad 57
Avocado
  celery, fennel and cherry tomato salad 102
  herbed chicken and potato salad with 32
  mayonnaise 103
Avocado oil 64

Balinese rice with peanut sauce 79
Banana and carrot cake 87
Basil
  pasta salad with pecan pesto 22
  preserved 42
  salad of summer vegetables with citrus vinaigrette and 77
  spaghetti with tomatoes and 24
  summer veal rolls with 33
Batter
  with beer 44
  with brandy 43
  tempura 94
Bean sprouts
  herbed slaw with 38
  stir-fried mushrooms and 71
Beans, tuna with 30
Beef
  en Daube 31
  stir-fried, with julienned vegetables 70
Bell pepper, see Capsicum
Blackberry muffins 89
Bread
  black and green olive 44
  cinnamon pumpkin 97
  extra cornbread 106
  Turkish flatbread 45
  walnut 55
Brown rice
  Balinese rice with peanut sauce 79
  healthy but delicious rice salad 53
  salad of nuts and 59
  soybean health loaf 86
  see also rice
Butter, cashew nut 93

Cabbage
  herbed slaw with sprouts 38
  wonton soup 66
Cake
  banana and carrot 87
  golden 97
Capsicum
  marinated goat cheese with roasted 18
  multi-capsicum salad 40
  shakshouka 17
Carrot and banana cake 87
Cashews
  devilled 73
  nut butter 93
Cauliflower, curried 85
Celery, fennel, avocado and cherry tomato salad 102
Champignons, marinated 101
Cheese
  cream cheese frosting 98
  French breadstick pizza 19
  garlic soup 14
  herbed goat, in olive oil 18
  herbed spinach 84
  marinated goat, with roasted capsicums 18
  pasta salad with walnuts 51
  spread, herb 92

INDEX

Cheese — *continued*
    suppli with olives and artichokes 20
    Truffa D'Auvergne 35
    see also Cottage; Parmesan
Chick peas
    falafel 21
    hummus 13
Chicken
    "fast-food" gourmet 49
    and potato salad with avocado, herbed 32
    satay with sesame seeds 75
    smoked, with poached pear and walnut salad 51
    southern 104
Chili
    oil 80
    prawns 74
    sauce, fried quail with 63
Chives, a relish of 105
Cinnamon pumpkin bread 97
Cioppino 14
Citrus vinaigrette 77
Coconut oil 64
Coleslaw with sprouts, herbed 38
Cookies, happiness 91
Corn oil 104–6
Cornbread, extra 106
Cottage cheese
    dressing, curried 106
    Truffa D'Auvergne 35
Cream cheese
    frosting 98
    herb cheese spread 92
Croutons, hazelnut 56

Date squares, crumble-crusted 88
Devilled cashews 73
Dipping sauce for tempura 94
Dressing
    curried cottage cheese 106
    for "fast-food" gourmet chicken 49
    hazelnut oil 59
    herbed raspberry vinegar 54
    olive oil 39
    for salad of baby greens 57
    for salad of brown rice and nuts 60
    for spiced seafood salad 67

    yoghurt salad 103
    see also Mayonnaise; Vinaigrette

Eggs
    aïoli 16
    avocado mayonnaise 103
    batter with beer 44
    batter with brandy 43
    mayonnaise 86
    omelette of spring herbs 83
    prawn and watercress vinaigrette platter 28
    relish of chives 105
    shakshouka 17
    spiced hard-boiled 12
    suppli with olives and artichokes 20

Falafel 21
Fish
    cioppino 14
    cutlets, grilled marinated 68
    marinated garfish fillets 24
    souvlaki 28
    with Szechwan sauce 68
    Tasmanian salmon tartare 26
    see also Prawns; Seafood
Flatbread, Turkish 45
French breadstick pizza 19
Frosting, cream cheese 98

Garbanzo beans, *see* Chick peas
Garfish fillets, marinated 24
Garlic
    parsley and tuna sauce 42
    soup 14
    vinaigrette 31
Goat cheese
    herbed, in olive oil 18
    marinated, with roasted capsicums 18
Golden cake 97
Grapeseed oil 99–103

Happiness cookies 91
Hazelnut croutons, salad of baby greens with pâté on 56

INDEX

Hazelnut oil 56
   dressing, wild rice salad with 59
   vinaigrette 58
Herb
   cheese spread 92
   chicken and potato salad with
      avocado 32
   cold herbed tomato sauce 41
   goat cheese in olive oil 18
   oil 107–9
   omelette of spring 83
   raspberry vinegar dressing 54
   slaw with sprouts 38
   spinach 84
Hummus 13

Lamb cutlets, tarragon 95
Leeks with olive oil and tomatoes 37

Maize oil, *see* Corn oil
Maple syrup and apple muffins 89
Mayonnaise 86
   avocado 103
Mexican rice 95
Muffins
   apple and maple syrup 89
   blackberry 89
Mushrooms
   and bean sprouts, stir-fried 71
   marinated champignons 101
   snow peas with water chestnuts and 76
Mustard sauce, rabbit with 75

Nut oils 47–61
   almond oil 61
   hazelnut 56–60
   pistachio oil 61
   walnut 47–55

Oil
   herb 107–9
   olive 4–9
   rosemary 109
   using and re-using 1–3
   see also Nut oils; Vegetable oils

Okra, stewed 34
Olive oil 4–46
Olives
   beef en daube 31
   bread, black and green 44
   gourmet pizza 48
   prawn and watercress vinaigrette platter 28
   shakshouka 17
   suppli with artichokes and 20
   tapenade 12
Omelette of spring herbs 83
Onion, confit of 36

Parmesan cheese
   gourmet pizza 48
   pasta salad with pecan pesto 22
   spaghetti with tomatoes and basil 24
Pasta
   salad with pecan pesto 22
   salad with smoked salmon and caviar 100
   salad with walnuts 51
Patties with tartar sauce, seafood 9
Peanut oil 73–80
Peanut sauce
   Balinese rice with 79
   spicy pork satays 82
Pear, smoked chicken with walnut salad and poached 51
Pecans
   green salad with toasted 52
   pasta salad with 51
Pesto, pasta salad with pecan 22
Pistachio oil 61
Pizza
   French breadstick 19
   gourmet 48
Pork
   spicy satays 81
   with water chestnuts 70
   wonton soup 66
Potato
   baked skins, with aïoli 15
   salad and herbed chicken with avocado 32
   Truffa D'Auvergne 35

INDEX

Prawns
  chili 74
  cioppino 14
  lemon-marinated 25
  pickled 74
  pil pil 27
  and watercress vinaigrette platter 28
Pumpkin cinnamon bread 97

Quail, fried with chili sauce 63

Rabbit with mustard sauce 75
Raspberry vinegar dressing, herbed 54
Rice
  Balinese, with peanut sauce 79
  Mexican 95
  salad, healthy but delicious 53
  salad of nuts and brown 59
  salad with hazelnut oil dressing, wild 59
  suppli with olives and artichokes 20
  see also Brown rice
Rosemary oil 109

Safflower oil 83–91
Salad
  for autumn 57
  of baby greens with pâté on hazelnut croutons 56
  celery, fennel, avocado and cherry tomato 102
  green, with toasted pecans 52
  herbed chicken and potato salad with avocado 32
  multi-capsicum 40
  pasta, with pecan pesto 22
  pasta, with smoked salmon and caviar 100
  rice, healthy but delicious 53
  spiced seafood 66
  of summer vegetables with basil and citrus vinaigrette 77
  tomatoes with crisp crouton 38
  vegetarian delight 39
  wild rice, with hazelnut oil dressing 59
Salad dressing, *see* dressing
Salmon
  marinated 29
  smoked, pasta salad with caviar and 100
  Tasmanian salmon tartare 26
Sandwich, supreme open 11
Satay
  with sesame seeds, chicken 75
  spicy pork 81
Sauce
  chili, fried quail with 63
  cold herbed tomato 41
  dipping, for tempura 94
  fish with Szechwan 68
  mustard, rabbit with 75
  parsley garlic and tuna 42
  peanut, Balinese rice with 79
  tartar 10
Seafood
  patties with tartar sauce 9
  salad, spiced 66
Sesame oil 65–72
Sesame seeds
  chicken satay with 75
  tahina 99
Shakshouka 17
Shrimps, *see* Prawns
Snow peas with water chestnuts and mushrooms 76
Soup
  cioppino 14
  garlic 14
  wonton 66
Souvlaki, fish 28
Soy oil 81–2
Soybean health loaf 86
Spaghetti with tomatoes and basil 24
  see also Pasta
Spinach, herbed 84
Spread, herb cheese 92
Sunflower oil 92–8
Suppli with olives and artichokes 20
Szechwan sauce 69

Tahina 99
Tapenade 12
Tarragon lamb cutlets 95
Tartar sauce 10
Tasmanian salmon tartare 26
Tempura 93

INDEX

Tomato
  celery, fennel and avocado salad 102
  with crisp crouton salad 38
  curried cauliflower 85
  French breadstick pizza 19
  gourmet pizza 48
  leeks with olive oil and 37
  Mexican rice 95
  sauce, cold herbed 41
  shakshouka 17
  spaghetti with basil and 24
  stewed okra 34
  vegetarian salad delight 39
Truffa D'Auvergne 35
Tuna
  with beans 30
  parsley and garlic sauce 42
Turkish flatbread 45

Veal rolls with basil, summer 33
Vegetable oils 62–106
  avocado oil 64
  coconut oil 64
  corn oil 104–6
  grapeseed oil 99–103
  peanut oil 73–80
  safflower oil 83–91
  sesame oil 65–72
  soy oil 81–2
  sunflower oil 92–8
Vegetables
  beef with julienned 70

  with citrus vinaigrette, salad of summer 77
Vinaigrette 2
  asparagus 16
  citrus 77
  garlic 31
  hazelnut oil 58
  walnut 52
  walnut oil 54

Walnut
  bread 55
  healthy but delicious rice salad 53
  pasta salad with 51
  salad, smoked chicken with poached pear and 51
  vinaigrette 52
Walnut oil 47–55
  herbed raspberry vinegar dressing 54
  vinaigrette 54
Water chestnuts
  pork with 70
  snow peas with mushrooms and 76
Watercress
  and prawn vinaigette platter 28
Wild rice salad with hazelnut oil dressing 59
Wonton soup 66

Yoghurt salad dressing 103